The Evolution of a *Creationist*

The
Evolution of a *Creationist*

by Dr. Jobe Martin

A LAYMAN'S GUIDE
to the conflict between

THE BIBLE

AND

EVOLUTIONARY THEORY

Biblical Discipleship Publishers
Rockwall, Texas

Published by
Biblical Discipleship Publishers
2212 Chisholm Trail
Rockwall, Texas 75032   (972) 771-0568

Library of Congress Cataloging-in-Publication Data

Martin, Jobe R. 1940-
    The Evolution of a Creationist

        320 p. cm.
        ISBN 978-1-6275801-1-3
        1. Religion-Christian. 2. Creation Science.
        3. Creation/Evolution debate. 4. Christian Gospel

I. Title II. Title: A Layman's Guide to the Conflict Between
the Bible and Evolutionary Theory

All Scripture quotations in this book are taken from the King
James Version of the Bible.

Eleventh Printing, Revised 2013, 150,000 in print

Printed in the United States of America

This book is dedicated to my
Creator and Savior,
the Lord Jesus Christ
To God alone be the glory.

*All who gave of their time
and talents in producing this book
did so by God's grace and for His eternal glory,
for our sufficiency comes from God
(2 Corinthians 3:5),
and without Him we can do nothing
(John 15:5b).*

TABLE OF
Contents

PREFACE

This book is a condensation and simplification of more than thirty years of studies that moved me from unquestioning belief in Darwinian evolution to undoubting trust in the special six-day creation by God as presented in the biblical account.

It is my conviction that a simple discussion of the major questions in the creation/evolution controversy is needed for those men and women who have little or no background in science. Thus, I have attempted to address pertinent issues as simply as possible—fully recognizing that those who have studied intensively in specialized areas of science may accuse this book of being too simplistic.

The book touches on the evolution of a creationist (me), but emphasizes the inherent conflicts between evolutionary theory and the Bible. This work is a compilation of thoughts and writings that God used to change my belief system, my worldview.

It is my conviction that the Old and New Testaments of the Bible are God's inspired, infallible, inerrant Word. The Bible is to be interpreted in the normal, historical, grammatical, literal fashion. Yes, the Bible uses figures of speech, but they are evident when used. The King James Version of the Bible is quoted throughout because of its universal acceptance. Some of you may not be familiar with King James English. In the quoted Scriptures you will notice pronouns referring to God are not capitalized and certain punctuations and capitalized words seem out of place. This is the way things were done in King James English (unless I have made a mistake in the transcript).

When I use the term "evolution," I am referring to the idea that after the "Big Bang" and after the earth was supposedly formed (by an accidental, mindless, totally random chance

10

process), it took millions of years to produce organic molecules and then many more millions of years of evolutionary processes (mutations and natural selection) to produce people (the molecules-to-life-to-man theory, also called macroevolution).

For those of you who read with extreme concentration, never missing a word or a thought, please overlook the repetitions. Some of us need repetition so that we can better understand a concept. Others of us do not have the time to read a book in one sitting. Therefore, I have purposely repeated certain things throughout the book for reinforcement.

When speaking about origins (Where did I come from?), we are dealing with a system of faith. It may be faith in eternal God or faith in eternal matter/energy. This book will attempt to help the reader discern which system of thought about our beginnings he or she believes. Is it the impersonal, plus chance, plus billions of years? Or is there an infinite Creator/Designer capable of creating the universe and all it contains in six 24-hour days about 6000 years ago?

Do we creationists have a different set of fossils, different living creatures and a different earth to study in contrast to the evolutionists? No, we study the same data. But how can two such opposite ideas come about if we are exposed to the identical information? The answers will be dealt with in the following pages. It has everything to do with your worldview—your basic set of beliefs and whether these beliefs include God.

If we say we are Christians, then we need to know what we can believe about the biblical account of creation, and not according to our politically correct humanistic evolutionistic culture. It is a shame that most professing Christians have joined the ranks of evolution via theistic evolution and progressive creationism. Even to this day, most Christians have never been exposed to biblical creationism. Many of God's people, when confronted with the evidences for biblical creationism, joyfully accept the truth.

I would encourage parents and young people to start building a personal library of good creationist literature. Helpful creationist books and organizations have been included for your reference. Many high school and college students are writing reports from a creationist perspective. Professors can appreciate excellently documented scholarship even when they disagree with the creationist's position.

It is a known fact that we Christians are losing 70% of our evangelical Christian young people by the end of four years of college. My friends with Campus Crusade for Christ claim that if they do not reach Christian college freshmen within their first six weeks on campus, they have already lost them to other worldviews. Christian youth are buying into other worldviews presented to them on the secular campuses. They are deserting their Christian roots by the thousands!

Most Humanist, Marxist, New Age, Islamic and Postmodern professors have an agenda—they want the minds and hearts of our kids! Most of us Christians do not have nearly as well defined an agenda. We send our children off to these schools and universities unable to defend their faith. As they go to various places for parts of their education, they should be equipped and ready to live out Scriptures such as 1 Peter 3: 13-17:

> **And who is he that will harm you, if ye be followers of that which is good? But and if ye suffer for righteousness' sake, happy are ye: and be not afraid of their terror, neither be troubled; But sanctify the Lord God in your hearts: and be ready always to give an answer to every man that asketh you a reason of the hope that is in you with meekness and fear: Having a good conscience; that, whereas they speak evil of you, as evildoers, they may be ashamed that falsely accuse**

your good conversation in Christ. For it is better, if the will of God be so, that ye suffer for well doing, than for evil doing.

We send our children out as <u>mission fields</u> rather than as <u>missionaries</u>! Many exuberant Christian youth are shipwrecked in their faith by the subtle and scientific-sounding arguments of evolution and the intimidation tactics of certain teachers and professors.

Dads and Moms, things in the classrooms are not at all like they were when we went to school! May I give you an example? A Christian student who graduated at the top of his class at a major secular university wrote a paper (5-1-2001) for his senior Microbiology course entitled, "Comparing and Contrasting the Regulation of the Lactose and Galactose Operons and Regulons in Streptococcus thermophilus, Streptococcus mutans and Lactococcus lactis." On the first page of his paper he made a HUGE mistake that sent his professor ballistic. The student wrote on his opening page, and I quote: "This genetic group-control mechanism is a wonderfully designed informational system…." And his professor launched into outer space!

What's the big problem? The student used the word "design." This implies "Designer" which implies "purpose" which smacks of "GOD." So here are the intimidating comments of the senior-level professor, and again I quote verbatim (exactly as the professor wrote):

Aaron-I suggest you grow up or think very hard about your major in Biology. Creationism is not science-it is not testable, it cannot predict future behavior.- [This paper is] poorly focused immature + pedantic much irrelevant information blatantly apologetic. Inappropriate for a science course. Poor science. Science is not anti-religion but your religion is clearly anti-science. Pick another field where personal opinions are all that matters. I suppose that my reaction will feed your martyr complex, but so be it. I too am a devout Christian. I believe the Bible is the inspired Word of God-I believe I am saved through the redeeming power of Christ Jesus. However, my faith is not simplistic, literalist, inconsistent, uninformed + prejudiced as yours appears to be. Again, think hard about your major and your course selections for the Fall.

Parents, do you see what I mean? With intimidation tactics like the ones above, the average Christian student raises the white flag, surrenders, and says, "Okay, Professor, what do you want me to believe?" We are losing 70% of our Christian kids. Our children are thoroughly confused by teachers who claim to be "Christian," but attack even the slightest hint that the student might really believe in God. It is worse if they believe in His biblical account of creation! These arguments are not limited to "science" classes, but are presented in such courses as freshman English, Physical Education, Sociology and Religion!

This book will attempt to point out the distinct differences between evolution and creation. Hopefully the readers will realize that the Biblical approach to the study of origins is trustworthy. The Bible is not exhaustive when it deals with science, but it is true.

My personal thanks go to all of the courageous authors who have influenced me and suffered for the sake of righteousness in their endeavors to glorify our Lord through their writings. The first book that I read on this subject (in 1971) impacted me greatly. It was *The Genesis Flood* by Dr. Henry Morris and Dr. John Whitcomb. The second book was written by Dr. Bolton Davidheizer and is entitled *Evolution and the Christian Faith*. These two books played a significant role in my evolution out of evolutionary thinking.

I know that apart from God's Spirit working within people's hearts to convict them of truth, mere human efforts to make an apologetic and change people's minds are futile. I also believe that the "Battle is the Lord's" (2 Chron. 20:15) and yet He somehow delights to use His saints in the battles—for His ultimate eternal glory. I humbly bow before my Creator and Savior, the Lord Jesus Christ, and am trusting Him to use His Word to speak to your heart. He is faithful (2 Tim. 2:13) and His Word is true (John 17:17) and living and powerful and sharper than any two-edged sword (Heb. 4:12) and will not return void (Isaiah 55:11). As God says in his revealed Word, the Bible, there will come a day when every knee will bow and every tongue confess that Jesus Christ is Lord to the glory of God the Father (Philippians 2:10, 11)! His truth will ultimately prevail—eternally!

MARVELS OF GOD'S CREATION

At the end of each chapter (and within some chapters), a "Marvel of God's Creation" will be inserted to display the uniqueness of certain creatures in God's creation. Evolutionary belief is based on the premise that through a series of chance mutations and natural selection, plants and animals evolve new parts and abilities as they are needed. Textbooks talk about fossil turtles and fossil cockroaches being several hundred million years old. And yet these fossil creatures look exactly like living turtles and cockroaches look today. So why have they not evolved and changed over the millions of years? "They were perfectly suited for their niche in nature and did not need to change." So evolution in life forms does not happen unless it needs to???

Evolution simply cannot explain the origin of the unique animals discussed in this book. There is no way their existence could have happened apart from special creation. They would have "died in process" trying to evolve the necessary equipment and functions to maintain life. Brilliant men have spent lifetimes attempting to prove that creatures evolved from and into other kinds of creatures. That job has yet to be accomplished!

AN ADMONITION

**If you have time to read
this book today, but have not
taken the time to read your Bible,
then you do not have time
to read this book!**

The Lord

By wisdom hath founded the earth;
 By understanding hath He established the heavens.
  By His knowledge the depths are broken up,
   and the clouds drop down the dew

(Proverbs 3:19,20).

1

THE EVOLUTION OF A CREATIONIST

Frustration was not an adequate word to describe my feelings! Which was true—evolution and billions of years, or creation in six 24-hour days? Two of my students at Baylor College of Dentistry had challenged me to investigate the possibility that the God of the Bible had created everything in six 24-hour days, as described in the first chapter of Genesis. My first reaction was, "Only an ignorant fool would believe in those ancient myths of the Book of Genesis."

I was an evolutionist. My years as a biology major at Bucknell University and a dental major at the University of Pittsburgh had convinced me that we are here because of evolutionary processes—all very logical and explainable through the Scientific Method. This was A.D. 1971! We were living in the days of modern, hi-tech-science, which had claimed proof of evolution to be true. And yet, these two dental students were brilliant young men. They held advanced degrees in the sciences. Surely, there must be a simple way to prove that their six-day view of creation was wrong. One of the questions those two dental students asked me was this: "Doctor Martin, have you ever heard of the concept of God creating things with the appearance of age?" At that point in my pilgrimage, I certainly had not, but it sparked a desire to learn more. And thus the frustration began.

FLASHBACK

The seed of my frustration was planted in September of 1966. I was attending USAF Basic Medical Training at Wichita Falls, Texas. It was the height of the Vietnam War. I had been given orders to report in at Andrews Air Force Base in Washington, D.C., upon completion of Basic Training. I was to be one of five dentists to serve the pilots and crews of President Johnson's presidential fleet—the 89th Military Airlift Wing.

The seed was a brief prayer. As I sat at the Officers Club that September night, I decided to clear things up with the God of the Bible (if He was really there). If He could part the Red Sea, turn water into wine, and raise the dead, He could answer a simple prayer. This was my prayer: "God, if You are up there, You have two choices. Either You can show me the girl I am going to marry, or You will see the wildest Air Force officer You have ever seen." I instantly thought, "Whew, nobody heard that prayer, I'm going out and live it up!"

Except God did hear that prayer. I met my wife-to-be that very day! We had a date the next night, and I told Jenna Dee that I was going to marry her on that first date. I knew I would. The God of the Bible had answered my specific prayer on the day that I uttered it to Him.

Upon my arrival to Washington, D.C., I decided to go to church and learn more about God. As I left church that first Sunday, the pastor shook my hand and asked if there was anything he could do to help me spiritually. I told him that anything he could do would help me spiritually, because at that point I was a big zero. Pastor Charlie Warford asked me to get up on Monday mornings at 6:00 a.m. and read the Bible with him. I used to like to argue with people about the Bible, but I'd never really read it. So, we read Matthew, Mark, and Luke, and we were in the gospel of John, chapter 3, verse 16, when God got my attention. This verse said, **"For God so**

loved the world, that he gave his only begotten Son, that whosoever believeth in him should not perish, but have everlasting life." It was the first phrase that got my attention. I was part of the world, had a heavy commitment to the world, and I knew it. That verse said to my heart that God loved me! I got on my knees with Pastor Warford, asked the Lord Jesus to forgive my sin and committed my life to Him. The seed had been planted and was beginning to sprout.

At the point in time I came to faith in Jesus Christ as my Savior, my sins were all forgiven, and I was given everlasting life. But something else happened which I was only later to realize. I had gone from being an "agnostic evolutionist" to being a "theistic evolutionist." That meant that now I believed in God <u>and</u> that He used evolution over billions of years to create the universe and everything in it. Somehow I did not understand, at this early stage in spiritual development, that pure naturalistic evolution absolutely eliminates God. I honestly believed that evolution was the only scientifically accurate option for how we got here. It was the "Big Bang," plus time, plus mindless random-chance processes. In other words, "nothing plus no one equals everything," or "slime plus time equals me."

EVERYONE BELIEVES BY FAITH

My university science professors had not told me that I was making some significant assumptions by believing in the Big Bang model. The big bang is the belief that the universe and all the matter it contained was once so densely compressed that the matter was invisible. This "cosmic speck" underwent a sudden mega-explosion that is labeled by evolutionary scientists as the "Big Bang."[1] Many scientists

---

[1] "The universe began as a particle that was infinitely dense and occupied no space." Robert Augros and George Stanciu, *The New Story of Science* (Lake Bluff, Illinois: Regnrey Gateway Pubs., 1984), pp. 54-64 (condensation and paraphrase).

believe that this explosion occurred between nine and twenty billion years ago. Just think of the tremendous, inexact range of time proposed by various evolutionists for the occurrence of this theoretical Big Bang…eleven-plus billion years!

To accept the Big Bang, one must assume that the existence of matter and energy is eternal—at least if you desire to be logical. Some evolutionists buy into the idea of quantum fluctuation (the idea that there was nothing there before the Big Bang and then, "BANG," and there was something). This seems like a large portion of imagination to me, but this is how quantum physics is trying to detour around the law of cause-and-effect! The Big Bang model, we are told, only attempts to explain the ordering of matter and energy, not their origin. Of course, explosions are most often observed to cause disorder, not order. Logically, if there is no God, matter had to be eternally present before the Big Bang or there would have been nothing there to go *BOOM!* We discover here that everyone on earth believes in something <u>eternal</u> by faith. It is either faith in eternal matter and energy, faith in an eternally reoccurring mystical quantum fluctuation <u>or</u> faith in eternal God.

FAITH IN CREATION OR IN EVOLUTION

Why is this belief by faith? Because it is beyond the reach of science to test. There are no experiments that can test who or what was here when the universe began. Consequently, when we speak of origins, neither the creation model nor the evolution model can be tested or verified by reproducible scientific experiments. This takes both models of origins out of the realm of science and into the arena of religiously-generated faith. Many evolutionists refuse to admit that their idea of the origin of all things is a faith-based system!

Theist and atheist both live by faith. Our basic set of beliefs, or system of faith, or way of thinking is our worldview. It is what we believe about life. Our worldview dictates our values and character. Behavior is the outward expression of our root worldview. When our children come home from school or college exhibiting a different type of behavior, it is because they are buying (or have bought) into a different religious worldview. How we view life, then, depends on what "worldview glasses" we are wearing (Proverbs 23:7). Are the worldview glasses we Christians are wearing influenced more by our culture or by the Bible?

Proverbs 14:12 says, **"There is a way which seemeth right unto a man, but the end thereof are the ways of death."** As we think about the creation/evolution controversy, what glasses are you wearing? Does it seem right to you, even as a Christian, to have on the evolutionary glasses of the humanistic worldview? In other words, if God says he created everything in a normal week, why do we become theistic evolutionists or progressive creationists and believe that God used the Big Bang and various forms of evolution over millions of years to create? We have been deeply tainted by the evolutionary culture in which we live! Rather than believing the Bible literally, we prefer to be "politically correct." Even we Christians seem to have **"loved the praise of men more than the praise of God"** (John 12:43 and 5:44).

ARE MATTER AND ENERGY ETERNAL?

Some evolutionists believe that if matter and energy were eternal, they would be—before the time of the big bang—in a state of equilibrium. Equilibrium means everything would be equal and non-reactive. A car is like that. The car sits there in neutral (equilibrium) and doesn't do anything until it is turned on. Starting the engine explodes the gasoline, which gives the power to move the car. Science tells us that when matter is somewhere for a long enough time (eternity past), it will eventually stop doing anything, all the possible reactions would have already occurred, and it would just sit there like a car in neutral. This is a part of the second law of thermodynamics that physicists call Zeroeth Entropy. Before the Big Bang, all matter and energy, if eternal, would be in neutral (equilibrium). It's like the car when it is turned off and in park on a flat driveway. It will not move until someone starts it up.

So, if everything was in neutral before the Big Bang, what made the Big Bang go *BOOM*? If you believe in the Big Bang and eternal matter and energy, you believe by faith that this infinitely dense speck of matter (which would have infinitely powerful gravity pulling inward) somehow overcame its own inward pulling forces and went "BANG," shooting its contents out, thus simultaneously creating time and space! This gargantuan cosmic explosion was of such a magnitude that it ultimately resulted in the production of all the contents of the universe. To make stars and galaxies and oceans and mountains and flowers seems to require un-random design and purpose. This has never been observed to occur through a chaotic explosion. Belief in a mega-explosion that ultimately results in order and regularity and predictability and beauty and music and emotions (such as love) appears to me to demand a huge volume of faith.

So, then, the question becomes either, "Do I believe by faith in eternal matter and energy?" (This gives me the problem of how did the Big Bang go *BOOM*?) or, "Do I believe by faith in eternal God?" Everyone believes by faith in something eternal.

Philip E. Johnson, a First Amendment attorney who taught law at the University of California, Berkeley, believes that the media all too often presents creationists as if they do not use or understand science. Johnson writes:

> In fact, there is a great deal more to the creation/evolution controversy than meets the eye, or rather than meets the carefully

cultivated media stereotype of "creationists" as Bible-quoting know-nothings who refuse to face up to the scientific evidence. The creationists may be wrong about many things, but they have at least one very important point to argue, a point that has been thoroughly obscured by all the attention paid to Noah's flood and other side issues. What science educators propose to teach as "evolution," and label as fact, is based not upon any incontrovertible empirical evidence (*scientifically proven facts, ed.*), but upon a highly controversial philosophical presupposition. The controversy over evolution is therefore not going to go away as people become better educated on the subject. On the contrary, the more people learn about the philosophical content of what scientists are calling the "fact of evolution," the less they are going to like it.[2]

Like many of us, Johnson is concerned that public school science teachers and university professors have moved out of the realm of "science" and into the sphere of religious teaching (faith) when they address the evolution of molecules to man as scientific fact. In my years as a science major at Bucknell University and the University of Pittsburgh, I was taught that science and fossils prove evolution to be true— that the important transitional steps in the evolution of one creature into another "occurred within its gaps." I now agree with Johnson when he questions current evolutionary theory and its adherents. The evolutionary model's "...mechanism accomplishes wonders of creativity not because the wonders can be demonstrated, but because they (evolutionists) cannot think of a more plausible explanation for the existence of wonders that does not involve an unacceptable creator, i.e., a being or force outside the world of Nature."[3] The political correctness of our day dictates the abhorrence of any credibility or reality to a literal God who is greater than science itself, even though He created true science!

[2] Philip E. Johnson, *Evolution as Dogma: The Establishment of Naturalism* (Dallas, TX: Haughton Publishing Company, 1990), pp. 1,2.

[3] Ibid., p. 7.

GOD, THE CREATOR

Though the idea of Creator God outside the world of nature is unacceptable to the majority of evolutionists, the Bible teaches that eternal God created the universe, and He did so *by* and *through* and *for* His only eternal Son, the Lord Jesus Christ. The eternal Son was there in the beginning of creation as can be seen in the plural pronouns of Genesis 1:26, **"Let *us* make man in *our* image, according to *our* likeness."** That He, the Son, was instrumental in the creation of all things is taught in the Gospel of John:

> **In the beginning was the Word and the Word was with God and the Word was God. The same was in the beginning with God. All things were made by him; and without him was not any thing made that was made. In him was life; and the life was the light of men (John 1:1-4).**

These verses of John verify that Jesus is the Creator, and that all things were made by Him. The book of Hebrews is another testimony that Jesus is the Creator of the world: **"God... Hath in these last days spoken to us by his Son, whom he hath appointed heir of all things, by whom also he made the worlds;..."** (Hebrews 1:1-2). The letter to the Colossians also refers to the Lord Jesus as the Creator of all things, and it goes on to name Him as the One Who holds all things together (Colossians 1:15-17).

Scientists say, "We have a problem. There are not enough stars and moons and asteroids to hold the universe together." This is called the "Missing Mass" problem. Everything should be flying apart, but it is staying together. A creationist can say, "I know what holds the universe together in spite of the 'Missing Mass' problem—the Lord Jesus, the Creator holds it all together by His great power" (Hebrews 1 and Colossians 1). When the Bible refers to science, it may not be exhaustive, but it is accurate. We can trust it.

When scientists choose to believe that God the Creator does not exist they are forced to come up with alternative explanations. They observe that our universe is holding together. They calculate that there is not enough mass to hold it together. Now they have a problem, so they must make up an alternative. In this case, the alternative I was taught in college in the late 50's was "invisible, cold, dark matter" holds the universe together. I was also taught that neutrinos (called by some scientists as "the smallest speck of reality in the universe") had no mass. But the most recent alternative to God's power holding everything together is neutrinos. It is now popular in some evolutionary circles to believe that neutrinos have so much mass that they hold the universe together, even though the mass of a neutrino has yet to be reliably established.

The Scriptures tell us that God holds the atom together and He holds the universe together. <u>The world came into being, not as a result of a chance, cosmic explosion, but as a special creation with a unique purpose.</u> God purposed to have people who would bring glory to Himself and with whom He could have fellowship. Ultimately, the Creator would step into time and His creation to become the Savior. But more about that later.

In the ancient Hebrew of the Old Testament, a word is repeated to emphasize it. For example, Isaiah 6:3 uses repetition to tell us that God is infinitely holy: ***"Holy, holy, holy* is the Lord of hosts, the whole earth is full of his glory."** You cannot get any holier than God. The Hebrew language uses the same word three times to show the total absolute holiness of God. In a similar way, Genesis emphasizes the fact of creation. Moses, under the inspiration of the Holy Spirit, writes:

> **This is the book of the generations of Adam. In the day that God <u>created</u> man, in the likeness of God made he him; Male**

and female <u>created</u> he them; and blessed them, and called their name Adam, in the day when they were <u>created</u> (Genesis 5:1-2, Emphasis added)

MAN, THE CREATED

Man was created, created, created! You cannot get any more emphatic than that. The Bible does not say man evolved, evolved, evolved. If God wanted to indicate that man had come about through ages of evolutionary changes, He surely could have. But His Word is Truth and the Truth says man was <u>created</u>. Mankind is not even Homo sapiens. Homo sapiens is a man-made term that puts us into the animal kingdom. We are created in the image of God distinctly above the animal kingdom to take dominion over the other life-forms on earth.

Not only did the Lord Jesus create man, He created man in God's own image. Did God, who "spoke the creation into existence," have to use millions of years of evolutionary mistakes to finally achieve His own image in man? Of course not! The millions of years idea further detracts from God's omnipotence.

If people really did evolve from monkey-like creatures, then the question arises, "What about the Virgin Mary? Was Mary, the human mother of the Lord Jesus, composed of made-over monkey genes?" If Mary was a highly evolved, distant relative of monkeys, then is our Lord also genetically related to the primates? Mary was created in the image of God, not in the lineage of monkeys.

The Bible tells us that God created man in His own image as an instant creation (Genesis 1:27). Jesus, the Creator, verifies this in Mark 10:6. He states: **"But from the beginning of the creation, God made them male and female."** The context of Mark 10:6 is divorce. We all know that cockroaches, rabbits and rats do not get divorces. The creator is talking about people. People get divorces. The Creator of one-man/one-woman 'til-death-do-us-part marriage tells us that divorce is not His solution to problems of pride and selfishness in marriage. (If you would like to read some of what the Bible says about this, please refer to Malachi 2:13-16; Deuteronomy 24:1-5; Matthew 5:31,32; Matthew 19:3-12; Mark 10:1-12; Luke 16:18; 1 Corinthians 7:10-16; Philippians 2:1-4; Ephesians 4:25-32; Colossians 3:12,13; 1 Peter 3:8,9; also www.biblicaldiscipleship.org.) People, created instantly in God's image, were there in the beginning.[4]

If we believe what the Bible says (and this book will argue that there is no "scientific" proof not to), Mark 10:6 alone destroys all evolutionary teaching. There were male and female people on earth from the beginning. The Creator says so. That leaves no room at all for billions of years of transitional animal forms (missing links) gradually evolving from a single cell through monkey-like creatures to man. [Remember: Evolution requires millions and billions of years, not just hundreds or even thousands. Large gaps of time in the genealogies in the Bible will be discussed later.]

MAN CREATED FULLY MATURE

If it is true that there were people here as male and female people from the very beginning, then God created them as instant adults. He created Adam, a full-grown (totally mature) adult who was only one second old. From Adam's rib (taken during the first general anesthetic!), God created instantly the first woman, Eve, complete and mature. Adam woke up and did not see a baby girl. He was introduced to Eve, his fully-grown wife. If you are a theistic evolutionist (one who believes that God used the Big Bang and the process of

---

[4] I heard this argument first on a tape dealing with the evolution/creation controversy by Floyd Jones Ministries, 8222 Glencliffe Lane, Houston, TX 77070.

evolution over millions of years to produce molecules, life and man), or even a progressive creationist (one who believes that God caused the Big Bang about 16 billion years ago and then progressively created everything over millions of years), you have a problem here. Do you know of any evolutionists that believe that women evolve from ribs? Genesis teaches that God made Eve from Adam's rib. Yes, this means that Eve was "sourced" in Adam, but she was still hand-fashioned from the rib that God took from Adam's side. If, as some progressive creationists claim, no rib surgery on Adam was involved, then why does it say that God **"...closed up the flesh..."** (Genesis 2:21b) in Adam after taking out one of his ribs?

If, when Adam first saw Eve, he would have asked, "Eve, how old are you?" she would have answered, "One minute old, Adam." She was created with full maturity. She looked perhaps 25 years old, but she had to wait a whole year to celebrate her first birthday. If Eve said, "Adam, I'm hungry," he could have reached out and picked a ripe peach, though its tree was only three days old. God also created fully mature trees. They looked old, and bore ripe fruit, but they were only three days old. These three-day-old trees were growing in soil that was created fully developed. In this soil, ferns were thriving and flowers blooming. Huge, minutes-to-hours old dinosaurs were walking the earth with Adam and Eve. (Fortunately, they ate plants and not people at this point. See Genesis 1:30.) Even the light beams from the stars could have been created at the instant God created the stars. It might appear to scientists that light from the farthest stars took millions of years to get to earth, but if God created fully mature systems, then that light beam may only be as old as the star itself.

When I am addressing the issue of creation with maturity (or the appearance of age) with a class of college students, invariably a hand will go up at that point of the discussion. The student will say, "Then your God is a liar. He created something that is not what it appears to be if He created Adam, Eve, and dinosaurs full-grown. They looked old, but were not old." No, God is not a liar. He told us exactly what He did in Genesis 1 and 2. When someone tells you what he or she is doing, it is not a lie. Our problem is that we do not think we can believe it as God describes it. Instead of believing the Bible, we have accepted the speculative theories of evolution.

Remember that in Hebrews 1, Colossians 1 and John 1, God tells us that Jesus is the Creator. Is it outside of the ability of God to create fully functional and mature systems? The Creator stepped into space-time-history as the Savior. He performed His first miracle during the wedding feast at Cana as recorded in John 2.

JESUS CREATED AGED WINE

Decades before Jesus and the Apostle John walked the streets of Cana, the Hebrew Old Testament was translated into Greek. This translation is called the LXX or the *Septuagint*. As John wrote the first two chapters of his gospel, he seemingly had in mind the first two chapters of the *Septuagint* (Old Testament in Greek). Not only is the use of the Greek language similar, but John 1 and Genesis 1 talk about the beginning of the world. John 2 and Genesis 2 deal with a man and a woman moving into marriage.

As recorded in John 2, the marriage party at Cana had run out of wine. There were six stone waterpots full of water, which Jesus turned into wine. The servants took some of this new wine to the headwaiter. After tasting it he said, **"Every man at the beginning doth set forth good wine; and when men have well drunk, then that which is worse; but thou hast kept the good wine until now"** (John 2:10).

How is good wine produced? It must be aged. How old was this wine? Only a minute or two. The Creator stepped into time and performed His first miracle and **"manifested forth his glory"** (John 2:11). He wanted His disciples to make no mistake as to who He is. In doing so, He created something (wine) with the appearance of age. (The Greek word for wine is "oinos," see: Ephesians 5:18; 1 Timothy 3:3, 8; Titus 2:3; Revelation 17:2; 18:3,13.) The seconds-old wine (oinos) tasted like aged wine. How many waterpots does the Biblical account of John record? Six! How many days did God work in the creation week? Six! As John writes his Gospel he could be thinking about Genesis 1 and 2. In Genesis, God spoke the universe into existence with full maturity in six days. In John 2, God created wine in a split second with full maturity in six waterpots.

Scripture has one interpretation; however, it can have many applications. One of the applications of John 2 is that the Creator does not need time. He can create whatever He wants to create and make it appear to "have some years" on it. Creations that are new can appear to have gone through a process that required time—but there was no time. Jesus manifested His glory as He performed His earthly miracles, without the use of time, just as He had created each aspect of the universe, instantly complete and fully functional without the use of time.

Some evolutionists teach that the Big Bang created time. The Bible says that God created time, that He is outside of time, but interacts with us in time. His miracles prove that He does not need time to do anything!

FEEDING THE FIVE THOUSAND

Jesus was moved with compassion. He decided to provide food to a large crowd. Did He say to His disciples, "Come on, guys, heat up the ovens. Today we are going to bake bread?"

The Lord Jesus fed 5,000 men (with women and children perhaps 15,000 total people), and He did it with five little loaves and two little fish. **"And they that did eat of the loaves were about five thousand men"** (Mark 6:44). If you had eaten that bread and did not know where it came from, might you have thought it had gone through a time process of mixing ingredients and baking? But there was no time!

PETER AIMS TO KILL

When Judas Iscariot came with a mob to betray Jesus, Peter grabbed a sword and aimed it at the head of one of them. The person may have ducked, and Peter succeeded in cutting off only the ear of Malchus, the servant of the high priest. (See: Matthew 26:51; Mark 14:47; John 18:10; Luke 22:50.) Dr. Luke, the physician, is the only Gospel writer that mentions Jesus miraculously restoring the ear: **"And one of them smote the servant of the high priest, and cut off his right ear. And Jesus answered and said, Suffer ye thus far. And he touched his ear, and healed him"** (Luke 22:50,51).

Did Jesus pick up the ear, get out His suture kit, sew the ear back on and say, "Come back in two weeks and we'll take out your stitches?" Of course not! He may have made a new ear or He put the old ear back on the person—no stitches, no scabs, no healing process, <u>no time involved</u>. See! The God of the Bible does not need time. There is no way to reattach an ear without the process of days of healing...unless you are God, infinite and sovereign, the Creator of time, space and life itself! Our Creator, the Lord Jesus, does not need time to do what we humans (limited and finite) would dogmatically say requires time!

DOES THE BIBLE TEACH BILLIONS OF YEARS?

In order to find a means to extend the Bible into billions of years, some Christians hold to the belief that there are big gaps in the genealogical tables in the Bible. Let's think about this for a minute. Everyone agrees there are about 2,000 years back to Christ the Lord. The commonly held figure for Abraham is around 4,170 years ago. No gaps here. So the gaps must be between Adam and Abraham.

Jude verse 14, 15 states:

> **And Enoch also, the <u>seventh from Adam</u>, prophesied of these saying, Behold, the Lord cometh with ten thousands of his saints, to execute judgment upon all, and to convince all that are ungodly among them of all their ungodly deeds which they have ungodly committed, and of all their hard speeches which ungodly sinners have spoken against him [Emphasis mine].**

There are seven continuous generations from Adam to Enoch according to Jude 14. There is nothing missing here. That means any gaps in the genealogical tables would have to be between Enoch and Abraham. Can we squeeze millions of years of evolutionary time between these two old patriarchs? The answer is a loud "NO!"

Noah's father, Lamech, was Adam's great, great, great, great, great, great grandson. They were one big, happy family. They all lived near each other and talked to each other. I can imagine Adam having his grandson Lamech sit in his lap as Adam said to him, "Lamech, your grandfather Adam should not have eaten of that fruit back in the Garden of Eden!" Then Lamech, years later, told his grandson, Shem (Noah's son), what Adam had told him.

Shem was with his father, Noah, on the ark and rode out the Flood. Many years passed and Abraham was born. Shem's lifespan overlapped Abraham's by 50 years or more. Shem assuredly taught Abraham all that Lamech had passed on to him that had come straight from Adam! There are no huge gaps of time in the genealogical tables to compensate for the long ages demanded by evolution (nor, I might add, are there big gaps of time in the transmission of God's Word). And even if there were gaps, they would not help make evolution possible, **since people are already here**. Evolution teaches that people were some of the very last critters on the evolutionary tree to evolve. Once Adam came on the scene, all the animals were already here, so there is nothing left to evolve.

Someone may have taught you that there were big gaps in the genealogical tables that gave room for evolution to happen. As you can see, gaps of time, if they were there, would not help evolutionize the Bible. Once Adam and Eve arrive on the scene, all other forms of life are already here. Remember, it was Adam who named all the kinds of birds and beasts on the sixth day (Genesis 2:20).

GOD CREATED TIME

God created time. He is not subject to it, since He is eternal and time is a created entity. One day "time will be no more." That is the message of 2 Peter 3:8, **"But, beloved, be not ignorant of this one thing, that one day is with the Lord as a thousand years, and a thousand years as one day."** How many times have people come up and said, "You know, the Bible teaches that those days in Genesis could be long periods of time. It says that a day is as a thousand years." 2 Peter 3:8, <u>does not teach</u> that each day of the creation week was 1,000 years or a longer period of time or vice versa (1,000 years as a day), but rather it shows that God is above time. The context of 2 Peter 3:8,9 is that time means nothing to God as He waits for us to come to repentance! I believe the God of the Bible shows some of the yearning of his heart in 2 Peter 3:8,9. As He waits for us to come to repentance, a day is like 1,000 years. On the day that we come to repentance, if He had waited 1,000 years it is as a day! The Creator Lord Jesus is not willing that any should perish (2 Peter 3:9).

Almost all of the miracles of our Creator appear to have needed time! But our Lord did not need time for His miracles, and He did not need time to create the universe. For us to believe that God created the universe in a literal six-day, 24-hour/day week about 6,000 years ago (as recorded in Genesis), we must assume that He can and will create things in their mature state. His miracles tell us that this is consistent with His power and His character. We can believe the Bible in the normal historical and grammatical sense of its meaning.

Could it be that molecules-to-man evolution is not based on true science, but upon many unprovable assumptions? We will consider this in Chapter Two, but one more thought first. The first verse of the Bible, Genesis 1:1, says: **"In the beginning God created the heavens and the earth."** The Hebrew word for "God" (Elohim) is a plural word, and the same word is sometimes translated "gods." The verb, created, is third person singular, "He Created" in the Hebrew. Did God make a grammatical mistake (the same as us saying "they was" which is not only incorrect English, it is very bad Hebrew!) in the very first verse of the Bible by putting a plural noun with a singular verb? Not at all! God is telling us, in His first written words to us, that He is a plurality and at the same time a singularity. He is the one true God in three persons: the Father, the Son and the Holy Spirit. He is the Almighty Trinitarian God of the Bible, the three-in-one!

God's universe speaks of His attributes. The singular universe is composed of three elements: space, time and matter (which includes energy). "In the beginning"—time, "God created the heavens"—space, "and the earth"—matter. The one, singular universe is a plural, a tri-unity (tri-unity is used instead of Trinity since only the God of the Bible is the Trinity). Space is a tri-unity composed of width, depth and height. Time is a tri-unity of past, present and future. Matter is a tri-unity of solid, liquid and gas! We are one person made up of three parts, a body, a soul and a spirit. The atom is composed of three major parts: protons, neutrons and electrons. This phenomenon of one entity that is divided into three goes all the way through the creation and screams of the special Trinitarian God of the Bible.

In one short verse (Genesis 1:1), the God of the Bible describes the fundamental aspects of His universe and portrays Himself as plural and singular at the same time! Therefore, we Christians are not polytheists (Hinduism and New Age), nor are we monotheists (Islam and Judaism). Christianity is unique among all other religious systems. Christians are Trinitarians. We are baptized **"...in the name** [singular] **of the Father, and of the Son, and of the Holy Ghost** [The One Who is Three]**"** (Matthew 28:19b).

WE CAN BELIEVE THE BIBLE!

As we will see in the chapters ahead, <u>there is no scientific reason not to believe the Holy Scriptures of the Bible as they are written</u>. Of course, I did not know these things back in 1971, and many years later I am still learning. As I talked with those Baylor students, I began to realize that evolutionary theory and the Biblical creation account cannot be merged. The belief that God used evolutionary processes or even successive creations over extended periods of time to change primitive molecules into you and me (Macroevolution, Theistic Evolution, Progressive Creation) is inadequate. It portrays a vicious, stupid God who needed millions of years of ferocious animals eating animals or "survival of the fittest," to produce something He considered perfect enough to announce that man was finally in His own image. Evolution destroys God, His infinite power and His image. Furthermore, evolution enslaves God to the restrictive boundaries of time and robs Him of His glory (Isaiah 48:11).

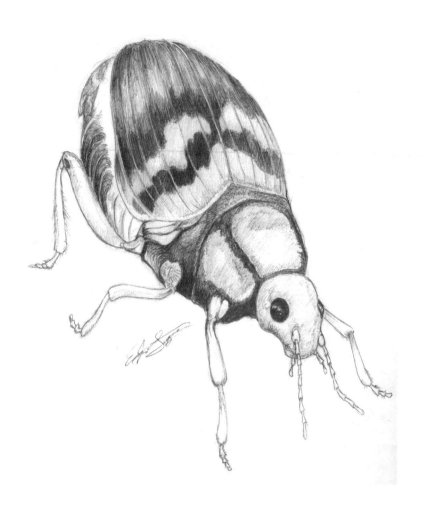

MARVEL OF GOD'S CREATION

#1

The Bombardier Beetle

If there is any creature on earth that could not possibly have evolved, that creature is the Bombardier Beetle. It needed God to create it with all its systems fully functional. The study of this incredible insect has been going on for many years. In 1928, authors C. L. Metcalf and R. L. Flint wrote: "The bombardier beetle, Brachinus, ejects an acrid fluid which is discharged with a distinct popping sound and a small cloud of vapor that looks like the smoke from a miniature cannon."[5] More recently, *Time Magazine* reports:

> ...the bombardier (beetle) does appear to be unique in the animal kingdom. Its defense system is extraordinarily intricate, a cross between tear gas and a tommy gun. When the beetle senses danger, it internally mixes enzymes contained in one body chamber with concentrated solutions of some rather harmless compounds, hydrogen peroxide and hydroquinones, confined to a second chamber. This generates a noxious spray of caustic benzoquinones, which explodes from its body at a boiling 212°F. What is more, the fluid is pumped through twin rear nozzles, which can be rotated, like a B-17's gun turret, to hit a hungry ant or frog with bull's eye accuracy.[6]

You might wonder how an evolutionist might explain this marvelous insect. Evolutionist Mark Isaak writes:

---

[5] C. L. Metcalf and W. P. Flint, *Destructive and Useful Insects*, 4th ed. (New York: McGraw-Hill, 1962), p. 24.

[6] Natalie Angier reported by Rick Thompson/San Francisco, *Time Magazine* (February 25, 1985), p. 70.

Do bombardier beetles look designed? Yes; they look like they were designed by evolution. Their features, behaviors, and distribution nicely fit the kinds of patterns that evolution creates. Nobody has yet found anything about any bombardier beetle which is incompatible with evolution.[7]

How does evolution, a mindless, undirected, purposeless, random chance process "create?" As Jewish scholar, Dr. Lee Spetner, writes:

> Randomness is an essential feature of NDT [neo-Darwinian theory]. There is no known physical or chemical mechanism to generate heritable variations that will improve adaptivity or increase the complexity of living organisms. The neo-Darwinians, therefore, had to choose randomness to produce the variations they needed. In this way they hoped that, through the direction afforded by natural selection, they could describe an evolutionary process that could account for a natural origin and development of life.
> The neo-Darwinians have rejected nonrandomness as the major feature of variation.[8]

Evolutionary theory has big problems when attempting to explain the existence and complexity of the bombardier beetle by means of random, chance happenings. Each stage in the evolution of its special chemicals would have led to its destruction. This one-half inch insect mixes chemicals that violently react to produce something similar to an explosion. How could the bombardier beetle have evolved such a complex means of defense without killing itself in the process? This problem has the members of the evolutionary establishment scratching their heads. Evolutionary theory says that you lose it if you don't use it. But, how do you use it unless you have it in completed and in fully functional form?

---

[7] "Bombardier Beetles and the Argument of Design," by Mark Isaak @www.talkorigins.org/faqs/bombardier.html.

[8] Lee Spetner, *Not By Chance!* (Brooklyn: Judaica Press, 1998), p. 209.

We have two options then. One is to believe that a mindless, random, chance process brought into existence exactly what would be essential for the creature to maintain life and defend itself. The other option is that God, in his sovereign wisdom, designed and created precisely what was needed for the welfare of the creature and encoded the information in its genes. With godless evolution, a new enzyme or chemical or organ or fin or beak or bone will have to randomly, mindlessly, unexplainably evolve until the creature gains its new improvement. As creationists, we would say that God created it just like it is, a discreet, fully functional little bug with an incredibly complex defense mechanism.

The bombardier beetle is irreducibly complex. Remember back in fourth grade when we reduced fractions down until they could be reduced no farther? This beetle cannot be reduced! If it doesn't have all its parts, it can't defend itself or, even worse, it could blow itself up. Naturally, it could not evolve after it blew itself up and was dead, so how did it get here? The evolutionists might say, "Mother nature, beneficial mutations, natural selection and time did it." Creationists would say, "God did it." (By the way, what or who is "Mother Nature" who does all these miraculous things?)

To prevent its own destruction, the little bug manufactures a chemical, called an inhibitor, and mixes it in with the reactive chemicals. But with the inhibitor, it would not be able to use the expulsion of hot, burning liquid and gases to discourage its enemies. A spider would eat it because the beetle has no solution to exploit to protect itself. Again, we have a dead beetle. Dead bugs cannot evolve the next chemical needed to release the protective reaction. That chemical turns out to be an anti-inhibitor.[9] When the anti-

---

[9] Duane T. Gish, *Creation Scientists Answer Their Critics* (El Cajon: Institute for Creation Research, 1993), pp.101-104.

inhibitor is added to the other chemicals, an explosive reaction does occur and the beetle is able to defend itself.

There is still another problem, however. The beetle must have an especially tough "combustion chamber." That chamber must have an outlet for the violent reaction to release its energy or once again, we have a dead bug. Problem solved: this unique creature has the necessary equipment, including twin-tail tubes to "exhaust" its defensive reaction. These tubes can be aimed at enemies in a 180° arc from straight to the rear, to directly toward the front. Amazingly, it does not shoot friendly creatures but only its enemies! How does a one-half inch long insect know how to aim at and shoot potential enemies?

When the little bug shoots its cannons (and it can shoot either side individually or both sides together) all we hear with our human ears is a "pop." But it is not just a single pop. It is a series of sequential pops that sequence so fast we only hear one "pop." If it was just one big POP, it would be like lighting the after-burners on a jet engine and the diminutive creature would blow itself out of the picture. But with a sequential pop it can hang on with its little legs and remain in place! Incredible!

How did its incredibly complex nervous system and advanced chemical system evolve? There is nothing exactly like bombardier beetles in the entire animal kingdom. Is this an example of the "impersonal, plus time, plus chance" or is it an example of a special, intricate creation by a God who is intimately involved with His creatures? Which system of belief can best explain the marvelous bombardier beetle: Evolution or Creation?[10]

---

[10] Duane Gish, Ph.D., *Dinosaurs Those Terrible Lizards* (San Diego: Creation Life Publishers), pp. 50-55. These pages describe the Bombardier Beetle. This children's book is primarily about dinosaurs. Also see Duane Gish, Ph.D., *Dinosaurs by Design* (Colorado Springs: Master Books, 1992), p. 83.

2

...AND THEN CAME ASSUMPTIONS

Many college science professors never tell their students that the evolutionary model of one cell to man is based on assumptions. What is an assumption? It is something taken for granted and supposed to be true.[11] As a six-day creationist, I believe God created the universe and everything in it fully mature (some creationists describe this as being created with the appearance of age). I cannot prove this with scientific experiments, so this belief is called an assumption. I suppose it to be true. Creationists assume God exists and that the Bible is His Revelation to mankind. (Now do not take me wrong here—I am speaking from the atheistic evolutionists' perspective. Make no mistake. God and his Word are truly knowable.)

Evolutionists likewise have assumptions. They take many necessary steps for granted in the molecules-to-man model. In other words, evolutionists assume that non-living chemicals gave rise to that first living cell which, in turn, mindlessly and randomly evolved into ever and ever more complex forms of life. There are no scientific experiments to prove the molecules-to-man scenario. Molecules-to-man is not scientifically testable or experimentally verifiable or reproducible or able to be authenticated in any way. And this

---

[11] *Webster's Third New International Dictionary* (Springfield, Mass., U.S.A: G. & C. Meriam Company, Publishers, 1981), p. 133.

is in spite of Carl Sagan and Isaac Asimov claiming on national television that evolution is no longer a theory but is the most well proven fact in all of science.

Writing as an evolutionist, G. A. Kerkut lists the major assumptions of evolution. These are the basic ideas an evolutionist "takes for granted" or "supposes" to be true. All of the "molecules-to-man science" is built upon these assumptions, but you rarely, if ever, see them listed in a high school or college textbook.

There are seven basic assumptions that are often not mentioned during discussions of evolution. Many evolutionists ignore the first six assumptions and only consider the seventh. The assumptions are as follows:

1. The first assumption is that non-living things gave rise to living material, i.e., spontaneous generation occurred.
2. The second assumption is that spontaneous generation occurred only once.
3. The third assumption is that viruses, bacteria, plants and animals are all related.
4. The fourth assumption is that protozoa (single-celled life forms) gave rise to metazoa (multiple-celled life forms).
5. The fifth assumption is that various invertebrate phyla are interrelated.
6. The sixth assumption is that the invertebrates gave rise to the vertebrates.
7. The seventh assumption is that within the vertebrates the fish gave rise to amphibia, the amphibia to reptiles and the reptiles to birds and mammals.[12]

MOLECULES-TO-MAN IS ASSUMED

What Dr. Kerkut has listed as "assumptions" is the whole of evolutionary teaching. In other words, there is no factual (experimentally testable and reproducible) science that supports evolution. The process of moving from non-living

---

[12] G. A. Kerkut, *Implications of Evolution* (New York: Pergamon Press, 1960), chapter 2, p. 6.

things to the first living, reproducing cell to man and giant Redwood trees is all an assumption.

Dr. Kerkut clearly states the evolutionary assumption that all life is related to that first cell. However, through the use of phase-electron microscopes, scientists have discovered that there are consistent differences in cellular substance in various kinds of animals. When studied microscopically, the living things of the evolutionary tree do not appear to be related to each other at all. In 1 Corinthians 15:39, the Bible reads: **"All flesh is not the same flesh: but there is one kind of flesh of men, another flesh of beasts, another of fishes, and another of birds."** This was written 1,900 years before scientists "discovered" the differences in the basic cellular components of the various kinds of living creatures. God created life and He sustains life! **"In him was life; and the life was the light of men. And the light shineth in darkness; and the darkness comprehended it not"** (John 1:4,5).

The Lord Jesus inspired His apostles and prophets to record details of His creation, which scientists are just beginning to discover. God says there are different types of flesh in the bodies of His earthly creatures. But there are also different types of heavenly bodies—the stars are different from each other and not the same as the sun or the moon (1 Cor. 15:41). [The Bible always differentiates between the sun, moon and stars. Much of what is known about stars has been learned by astronomers as they study our sun, which they assume is a star. But the Word of God, the Bible, never calls our sun, a "star." Therefore, much of what we think we know about stars may be completely wrong!]

Astronomers estimate there may be one trillion trillion stars. The best English dictionaries have less than one and a half million words. Yet, the God of the Bible has a name and a number for each star, **"He calleth them all by names"**

(Isaiah 40:26)! That is more than one trillion trillion names. God is infinite in His power and wisdom. If we used every word in the English language we could name less than .001% of the vast number of stars!

From the biggest star to the smallest atom, the magnitude and complexity of the universe is unexplainable, except in terms of a Creative Designer who is infinitely above any "chance processes" or human technology. The Creator-God designed His creation in such a way that as mankind studies it, he must either give God thanks and honor Him, or be reduced to foolish speculations and "vain imaginations" (Romans 1). This writer believes that macroevolution is a foolish speculation. It is in truth Speculative Philosophy, not verifiable science.

LIFE FROM DEAD CHEMICALS?

Many scientists assume life came from non-living chemicals[13] and that this only happened once. They say that everything we see alive, whether plant or animal, came from that first, primordial, single cell. Most evolutionists do not believe that one kind of life began in the Amazon and another in Africa and another in Arizona. They believe non-living chemicals gave birth to life in one cell at one particular place, and that cell learned how to reproduce itself before it died. That first cell became the ancestor of the entire plant and animal kingdoms.

The most well proven law of the biological sciences is called the Law of Biogenesis. This law states that life comes from life! Anything that is alive came from something else

---

[13] *The Mystery of Life's Origin* presents the scientific position that chemical evolution is impossible. This book by Doctors of Chemistry has not been answered by the evolutionists. Non-living chemicals will not ultimately generate reproducing life. The chemistry does not work that way [Charles Thaxton, Walter Bradley, Roger Olsen, *The Mystery of Life's Origin: Reassessing Current Theories* (N.Y.: Philosophical Library, Inc., 1984)].

that is alive. It states that life does not come from dead chemicals.

Why do evolutionary scientists assume the reality of this startling event of life from lifeless chemicals? "Because we are here and alive and so it had to have happened at least once since there is no Creator-God." The chances of life evolving from non-life are so astronomically high as to be impossible without a supernatural Lifegiver.

LIFE BY CHANCE?

Dr. Henry Morris and Dr. Gary Parker of the Institute for Creation Research have recorded the probability of the chance origin of life in their revised book, *What is Creation Science?* (pp. 269-276). If the entire universe were crammed with electrons (electron particles), the maximum number of these little particles would be ten to the power of 130. If each particle could do one hundred billion-billion events (steps in ever onward and upward evolution) every second for 3,000 billion years (100 times older than anyone says the universe is), then in the span of history of the universe, ten to the 170th power events could possibly happen. But to get a series of even 1,500 events to happen in order (and without God's help), events that might be moving from non-living chemicals to a living cell, there is only one chance in ten to the power of 450! This means that the probability of godless evolution even getting started is zero. [There is a law of probability that states that anything beyond ten to the fiftieth power (really minus fiftieth power—but that comes out in fractions and most people do not like to work with fractions) is impossible!] There aren't enough electrons in the universe to generate by chance a single living cell of a single evolutionary scientist. And yet, these scientists who refuse to believe in God are here. How did they get here? Without belief in God, the only option these people have is the purposeless, mindless evolution of non-living chemicals over aeons of time into a living cell and ultimately into man.

For nearly 150 years, some of the most brilliant scientists in the world have attempted to convert non-living chemicals into some form of reproducible life. No one has done it.

A CELL IS NOT SIMPLE

A single reproducible cell is far from simple. Dr. Leon Long, of the Department of Geological Sciences at the University of Texas at Austin, writes as an evolutionist:

> Among the first organisms were the lowly bacteria and blue-green algae. They are about as simple as a self-sufficient cell can be, which is none too simple, considering that a bacterium can synthesize some 3,000 to 6,000 compounds at a rate of about 1 million reactions per second! Cells of bacteria and blue-green algae contain just a single molecule of DNA, and they lack well-defined internal structures, such as a nucleus, chromosomes, and internal membranes.[14]

Is it any wonder scientists claim that life from non-living chemicals only happened once? According to Dr. Long, the simplest forms of life can perform one million reactions per second! Something that complex obviously had a designer and, therefore, needed the Creator Lord Jesus.

Scientists do not talk very much about the evolution of the cell membrane. The membrane that provides the outside wall (or skin) of the cell is highly complex. This membrane permits specific concentrations of certain chemicals and solutions into and out of the cell. If the concentrations of some of these chemicals vary by even 1/100%, an extremely tiny amount, the cell will die. At a microscopic spot in the universe, how did those chemicals all get together in the correct configurations and concentrations <u>and</u> at the same

---

[14] Leon E. Long, *Geology* (New York: McGraw-Hill Book Company, 1974), p. 172.

instant? In addition, how did the cell membrane form around them at just the right moment permitting only specific concentrations of chemicals in and out of the cell ("knowing," of course, what those chemicals must and must not be)? And how could all of this somehow know how to reproduce itself and not die in the process?

The God of the Bible said He *created, created, created*! His creation defies the speculations of the evolutionist. Creation necessitates a designer. It demands fully functional life from the beginning. Biology acknowledges this with its most well-proven law, the law of Biogenesis: Life generates life. If something is alive, it is alive because something else alive produced it. The Bible tells us the living God is the Creator of life, and that statement agrees with what we see in biology. Life always comes from life. In speaking of Jesus, the Bible says, **"In him was life and the life was the light of men"** (John 1:4).

And yet, evolutionary chemists construct laboratory experiments that attempt to display the means by which life began without God. Many of these experimenters believe that the atmosphere of primitive Earth was quite different than it is today. The atmosphere of the planet Jupiter is thought to resemble that of early Earth. Water vapor, hydrogen, ammonia and methane were the supposed ingredients. In a well-known experiment (in 1953), Dr. Stanley Miller, placed the above four ingredients into a glass jar which he heated and into which he sent sparks of electricity. He noticed a pink fluid coming off into his trap. This fluid contained some amino acids. Amino acids are the building blocks of proteins. Proteins are very much a part of living tissue, **but they are not life**.

Too much credit is given for the Miller experiment. It did not produce the correct mixture of amino acids necessary for life. Miller actually produced a poisonous mixture of amino acids—AND he cheated—he used intelligent design, not random, mindless, accidental, non-purposeful processes, further demonstrating the need for intelligence in the generation of life-building chemicals!

The Miller-type experiments do not display chemicals marching ever onward and upward until reproducing life is generated; yet evolution in this manner is assumed to have happened. As a matter of fact, there is no evidence in the rocks of Earth or the present oceans that water vapor, hydrogen, ammonia and methane ever existed in the concentrations necessary for Miller's experiments to accurately occur in nature.

The claim that chemical evolution is impossible, as presented in *The Mystery of Life's Origin*[13] by Dr. Charles Thaxton, has yet to be refuted. Random chemical reactions do not produce life! Dr. Stanley Miller and his followers did not produce anything with raw chemicals that even approaches life. Dennis Petersen in his informative book, *Unlocking the Mysteries of Creation*,[15] page 67, quotes Dr. Henry Morris who says it this way:

Unknown chemicals in the primordial past...through...
Unknown processes which no longer exist...produced...
Unknown life forms which are not to be found but could through...
Unknown reproduction methods spawn new life...in an...
Unknown atmospheric composition...in an...
Unknown oceanic soup complex...at an...
Unknown time and place.

Prove any of these unknowns of evolution with experimentally testable, reproducible science and the Nobel Science prize will be yours!

---

[15] Dennis R. Petersen, *Unlocking the Mysteries of Creation*, Vol. 1 (El Cajon: Master Books, 1988), p. 63, as quoted from the *Bible Science Newsletter*, May 1974, p. 8.

A PERSONAL GOD CREATES LIFE

The atheistic evolutionist says there was no God, no higher power, no designer, and no person behind the beginning of life. It was the impersonal (no person, therefore mindless), plus time, plus random chance (or, no one plus nothing equals everything). So, even if the Stanley Miller experiments did prove chemical evolution is possible, which they did not do, you still have a personal designer (Miller) making his creation. Does a personal designer-scientist, doing experiments in a carefully controlled laboratory, prove that the creation of life occurred without any creator designer (no God) in a totally random-chance primordial ooze? NO! Our God is worthy to receive honor and glory and praise because He created all things (Rev. 4:11). We can trust God and His Word, the Bible. Nothing is too difficult for Him (Jeremiah 32:17,27). He is the God of the impossible (Luke 1:37).

HAS ANYONE SEEN AN ELECTRON?

One of the greatest scientists of the space age, Dr. Werner von Braun stated:

> One cannot be exposed to the law and order of the universe without concluding that there must be design and purpose behind it all.... The better we understand the intricacies of the universe and all it harbors, the more reason we have found to marvel at the inherent design upon which it is based....
>
> To be forced to believe only one conclusion—that everything in the universe happened by chance—would violate the very objectivity of science itself.... What random process could produce the brains of man or the system of the human eye? They (evolutionists) challenge science to prove the existence of God. But must we really light a candle to see the sun? ...They say they cannot visualize a designer. Well, can a physicist visualize an electron? ...What strange rationale makes some physicists accept the inconceivable electron as real while refusing to accept the reality of a Designer on the ground that they cannot conceive Him?[15]

Ask any scientist if he believes in electrons. He will answer, "Certainly." Ask that same scientist if he or she has ever seen an electron, and they will say, "No." Scientists believe in electrons by faith as they observe the results of electron activity.

Is this not similar to faith in God? We do not see God, but we do "see" Him through His handiwork, the creation. Romans 1 explains that as we study the intricacies of the macro and micro universes, we should think about who designed them, who makes them work, and who holds them together.

FOOLISH SPECULATIONS

When scientists examine the largest stars and the smallest atoms and do not honor God as their Creator and give thanks to Him, they are reduced to foolish speculations and vain imaginations (Romans 1:18-23). Could the evolution of man from a single cell be a foolish speculation? Dr. Harrison Matthews, evolutionist and the writer of the introduction to the 1971 edition of Darwin's *Origin of Species by Means of Natural Selection or the Preservation of Favoured Races in the Struggle for Life*, states:

> The fact of evolution is the backbone of biology, and biology is thus in the peculiar position of being a science founded on an unproved theory—is it then a science or a faith? Belief in the theory of evolution is thus exactly parallel to belief in special creation—both are concepts which believers know to be true, but neither, up to the present, has been capable of proof.[16]

---

[16] L. Harrison Matthews, FRS, "Introduction," Charles Darwin, *Origin of Species by Means of Natural Selection or the Preservation of Favoured Races in the Struggle for Life* (London: J.M. Dent and Sons, 1971), p. xi, as quoted in *The Revised Quote Book*, ed. Andrew Snelling, Ph.D. (Institute for Creation Research, P.O. Box 2667, El Cajon, Calif. 92021), p. 2. For many more quotes that negate evolution from the literature of the evolutionary scientists, purchase *The Quote Book*. The cost is around $4.00 and well worth it.

Let's examine what Dr. Matthews is doing. He goes from fact to unproved theory to faith to belief, and all in one paragraph! But notice he is an honest evolutionist when he notes that evolution has no scientific proof. It is a speculation of faith. Yet, Dr. Ernst Mayr, professor emeritus of Harvard University, writes:

> Since Darwin, every *knowing* person agrees man descended from the apes. Today, there is no such thing as the theory of evolution. It is the fact of evolution (Emphasis in original).[17]

In his writing in *Omni Magazine* (which promotes evolution), Dr. Mayr presents godless evolution as fact, even though the Creator says in Romans 1 that all men know better: **"For the wrath of God is revealed from heaven against all ungodliness and unrighteousness of men, who hold** (suppress) **the truth in unrighteousness; Because that which may be known of God is manifest in them; for God hath shewed it unto them"** (Romans 1:18-19). Romans 1:22 adds: **"Professing themselves to be wise, they became fools."**

Dr. T. N. Tahmisian of the Atomic Energy Commission agrees:

> Scientists who go about teaching that evolution is a fact of life are great con men, and the story they are telling may be the greatest hoax ever. In explaining evolution, we do not have one iota of fact.[18]

Isaac Asimov, Carl Sagan, Ernst Mayr and others have presented evolution as no longer a theory, but a proven fact. They have done this without a single iota of fact. Evolutionist, D.M.S. Watson said it best:

---

[17] Dr. Ernst Mayr, *Omni Magazine*, February 1983, p. 74.

[18] Dr. T. N. Tahmisian, "The Fresno Bee," August 20, 1959, as quoted in *The Revised Quote Book*, p. 5.

Evolution itself is accepted by zoologists not because it has been observed to occur or is supported by logically coherent arguments, but because...no alternative explanation is credible.

Whilst the fact of evolution is accepted by every biologist, the mode in which it has occurred and the mechanism by which it has been brought about are still disputable.

...the theory of evolution itself is a theory universally accepted not because it can be proved by logical coherent evidence to be true but because the only alternative is special creation, which is clearly incredible.[19]

Dr. Watson clearly identifies the real problem in the evolution/creation controversy—it is God! Watson explains that there is no "logically coherent" science to support evolution, but that the only alternative is special creation, which he labels as "clearly incredible." In other words, he would rather believe in an idea that has no credible science to back it up than to believe in Creator Lord Jesus.

At this point, someone might object and say that Dr. Watson is speaking in 1929 and that evolutionary science has found many evidences since then to support it. Well, let's come up closer to the present and see if times have changed very much by 1997. Harvard professor Richard Lewontin, a confirmed evolutionist, writes:

...we have a prior commitment, a commitment to materialism. It is not that the methods and institutions of science somehow compel us to accept a material explanation of the phenomenal world, but, on the contrary, that we are forced by our a priori adherence to material causes to create a set of concepts that produce material explanations, no matter how counter-intuitive, no matter how mystifying to the uninitiated. Moreover, that materialism is an absolute, for we cannot allow a Divine Foot in the door.[20]

---

[19] D.M.S. Watson, "Adaptation," *Nature*, August 10, 1929, Vol. 124, #3119, pp. 231, 233.

[20] Richard Lewontin, "Billions and Billions of Demons," *The New York Review of Books*, January 9, 1997, p. 31

Obviously the issue is still Creator Lord Jesus Christ! Dr. Lewontin admits that to believe in evolution is counter-intuitive and mystifying. So why does he remain an evolutionist in spite of his own scientific evidence against it? He refuses to believe in God, his Creator!

According to *World* magazine, February 26, 2000, page 32, another evolutionist agrees with Lewontin:

> Kansas State University immunologist Scott C. Todd struck precisely the same note, [as Lewontin, Ed.] writing shortly after the [Kansas] Board of Education made its decision. In a letter published in the September issue of Nature, he declared that "Even if all the data point to an intelligent designer, such an hypothesis is excluded from science because it is not naturalistic."
>
> Though Mr. Lewontin calls his dogma materialism while Mr. Todd calls it naturalism, they are speaking of the same thing: the atheistic faith that nature means matter, and nature is all there is.

The real issue in the evolution/creation controversy is still God!!! The clearly incredible Creator says in Psalm 19:1:

The heavens declare the glory of God; and the firmament sheweth His handiwork.

MARVEL OF GOD'S CREATION

#2

The Incubator Bird

The Megapode or "incubator bird" of Australia is unique among birds. This three to four pound bird resembles a chicken or a small turkey. Some native Australians call it the brush turkey.

The incubator birds are unlike all other birds. So, if they evolved, from what did they evolve? Or what are they evolving into? An article in *Scientific American*[21] offers precious little by way of an evolutionary explanation for the origins of this strange bird.

All birds use body heat to incubate their eggs except the incubator bird.

> Instead, they pile up great heaps of debris which serve as incubators; the warmth of the fermenting compost does the work. In one species, the scrub fowl, a mound 20 feet high and 50 feet wide has been reported.[22]

Instead of using its own body heat to incubate its eggs (as does the chicken who sits on her eggs), the incubator bird uses fermentation heat and "some use solar heat and others the heat produced by volcanic action."[23]

---

[21] Roger S. Seymour, "The Brush Turkey," *Scientific American*, Vol. 265, No. 6, December 1991, pp. 108-114.

[22] Roger Tory Petersen, *Life Nature Library: The Birds* (New York: Time-Life Books, 1973), p. 140.

[23] *The New Encyclopedia Britannica*, Vol. 7 (Chicago: University of Chicago, 1990 edition), p. 1011.

A bird that uses volcanic heat or the warmth of fermenting plant life to hatch its eggs: Incredible! If there are any creatures that could not possibly evolve, the Australian incubator bird joins the bombardier beetle as such a creature.

The female is responsible for two activities. First, she must test the nest to be sure it is adequate for incubating her eggs. What explanation can evolution offer for the ability of the hen to evaluate the suitability of a nest that may be dug three feet into the ground and extend 15 feet or more above ground and up to 50 feet across? And what would motivate a little three and one-half pound male bird to get busy constructing monstrous nest number two, should the hen reject his first effort?

After accepting the nest, the second responsibility of the female is performed. She lays 20 to 35 eggs at the rate of one egg every three days for up to seven months. "As many as 16 eggs can exist in a normal mound at any one time."[24] Each egg weighs about a half a pound and is as large as an ostrich egg. That is a tremendous amount of work for a three to four pound hen. No wonder that upon completion of her laying task, she leaves the nest, never to return. She takes no part in the incubation and raising of her chicks. This is not your normal evolutionary way!

At this point, the male begins to perform his God-given job of managing the incubation of the deeply buried eggs. For this species of incubator bird chicks to survive, they demand a precise temperature of 91°F. Yes, exactly 91°F. If the male bird wants the chicks to survive, he will not let the temperature vary more than one or two degrees on either side of 91°F! How does the daddy bird maintain a consistent temperature of 91°F in a mound of decaying plants and dirt?

Scientists differ on the mechanism they think the bird uses to measure the temperature. Some think the bird's

---

[24] Seymour, p. 109.

thermometer is in its beak. Others believe the tongue can distinguish 91°F and a few tenths of a percent above and below 91°F.

Here is the point: How could a bird evolve the ability to precisely measure temperatures with its beak or tongue? Evolution has no credible answer. How would the incubator bird know it needed to keep its eggs at 91°F? The chicks would get too hot or too cold and die before he figured it out. And dead creatures do not evolve into higher forms.

You may be asking, "Well, how does this bird keep those eggs at 91°F?" The male digs down into the nest and checks the temperature. On hot days, he may pile extra sand on top of the nest to shield it from the sun. He may even rearrange the entire pile of rotting leaves and grasses several times a day.

On cooler days, the male megapodes (which means big feet) will push material off the top of the nest to permit more sunlight to penetrate the decaying organic material. Or, to keep the humidity at 99.5% around the eggs, he may dig conical holes toward the eggs to get more moisture deeper into the nest. Keeping temperature and humidity just right is a big job. Concerning the precision needed for incubation temperature maintenance, Seymour writes:

> This process is very precise: one centimeter of fresh material added to the mound can increase core temperature about 1½°C.[25]

Not only must the eggs be kept at 91°F and 99.5% humidity, but the chick must get enough air to breathe. The father provides the fresh air for the chicks as he daily digs down to the eggs. But the chick must get the air inside the shell. The means to get air inside the shell was provided by the hen as she formed the shell. It has thousands of tiny holes (called pores) in it. These holes in the thick shell (in at least

[25] Seymour, p. 110.

one species) are shaped like conical ice cream cones with the narrowest part of the cone toward the chick. As the chick grows, it cannot get enough air through the bottom of the cone so it begins to remove the inside layer of the shell. As it thins out the shell, the holes get bigger (moving up the cone) and the chick can get more air. Amazing!

The way the chicks hatch is also unique among birds. Unlike other birds, they are ready to fly with full feathers as soon as they break out of the egg. Only once they hatch, it takes up to three days for them to dig their way up out of the mound. How do they know they must dig their way out or else they die? How do they know which way to dig? They have not been instructed by either parent. Even so, they lie on their backs and dig up until they break out. Clearly, the God of the Bible is involved with all aspects of His creation! It is illogical to think of these incredible birds as a product of mindless, random, accidental, purposeless chance happenings of some mysterious evolutionary process over massive amounts of time.

Once the chicks dig out of the nest, they are on their own. They are not fed or cared for by either parent. When they are mature, the male will build a huge nest as an incubator for his mate's eggs. He will build this huge, precise mound without any instruction from his parents. This is not learned behavior! How does the brush turkey know the importance of 91°F?

Credentialed men and women have the audacity to say that this bird is the product of mindless, purposeless, random chance processes over long periods of time. But truly, how could the incubator bird even exist? Only if the God of the Bible lives and is involved with life-giving to His creatures.

3

HAS GOD BEEN TOPPLED?

One day my two creationist dental students asked me to give them a scientific explanation for how evolution occurs. In other words, they wanted me to defend my evolutionary beliefs by telling them the scientific evidence I could present as proof of how one creature evolves into another and whether that evidence conflicts with the Bible. Darwin seemed like the logical place to start searching for my answer. I believed the evidence was there somewhere, but I'd never been asked to prove it before. Did I ever get a shock! Darwin had no idea how one species of animal could evolve into another. He wrote to a friend in 1863:

> When we descend to details we can prove that no one species has changed (i.e., we cannot prove that a single species has changed): nor can we prove that the supposed changes are beneficial, which is the groundwork of the theory. Nor can we explain why some species have changed and others have not. The latter case seems to me hardly more difficult to understand precisely and in detail than the former case of supposed change.[26]

THE REALLY BIG QUESTION

Obviously, in 1863, four years after publishing *Origin of Species by Means of Natural Selection or the Preservation of Favoured Races in the Struggle for Life*, Darwin had no idea how one species might change into another. The only thing he

---

[26] Frances Darwin (ed.), *The Life and Letters of Charles Darwin* (N.Y.: Appleton & Co., 1898), Vol. 11, p. 210 (Darwin's letter to G. Benham, May 22, 1863).

thought he could prove was that "...no one species has changed." He could not even imagine what a "beneficial" change might look like. Scientists today remain as baffled as Darwin. The world's leading evolutionary thinkers had a convention in Rome in 1981. They wanted to decide what makes one species evolve into another species, and how that change, from one animal or plant into another, might occur. Dr. Ernst Mayr, professor emeritus of Harvard, writes:

> We had an international conference in Rome in 1981 on the mechanisms of speciation. It was attended by many of the leading botanists, zoologists, paleontologists, geneticists, cytologists and biologists. The one thing on which they all agreed was that we still have absolutely no idea what happens genetically during speciation. That's a damning statement, but it's the truth.[27]

These scientists in Rome in 1981 arrived at their conclusion, "We have no idea how evolution of one species into another occurs!" Neither did Darwin in 1863! This, then, is the really big question of evolution: How does it happen? God says He created each thing "after its kind" (Genesis 1:11, 12, 21, 24, 25). Evolutionists say they do not know how "kinds" come into being. Which account do you believe: God's or the evolutionist's? My position is that God alone is worthy to be praised!

Scientists do not know how one kind of life-form might change into another. They do not even know how a simple chemical compound might come about. Author and friend of evolution, Jeff Goldberg, records for us the thoughts of Hans Kosterlitz, one of the discoverers of the human body's natural pain killers, the enkephalins:

---

27 Dr. Ernst Mayr, *Omni Magazine*, February 1983, p. 78.

It is a question almost of God. Working on the enkephalins you get—without being religious—a commitment. You start to admire and wonder. How could that come about—that plants and animals share such structurally similar chemicals? How, even after a million years of evolution, could the earth, with all its plants and creatures, be so very simple and unified?[28]

Kosterlitz looked at the enkephalins, and his study of the micro-universe made him think about God. But he quickly adds the disclaimer "without being religious," as if thinking about God is not religious when studying only a small part of His creation. Apparently Kosterlitz believes God has nothing to do with science. Yet, when scientists study specific aspects of the creation, God's intention is for them to realize that there must be a Designer-God behind it all. However, most add their disclaimers and refuse to honor Creator Lord Jesus as God. God's Word (i.e. Romans 1:18-22) declares that their thinking is thereby reduced to vain imaginations and foolish speculations (evolution over millions of years, etc.).

Kosterlitz questioned how plants and animals could "...share such structurally similar chemicals." If we examine this sharing of chemicals from a creationist perspective, then God created life to fit in the common atmosphere of earth with a common food chain composed of certain basic chemicals. Similarities in creatures do not prove evolution, but more logically display the wisdom of God in creating plants and animals, which, in all their diversity, can exist in a common environment. [More about the Anthropic Principle later.] God designed all life to exist while using a few common basic chemicals in an atmosphere made mostly of oxygen and nitrogen. What genius the God of the Bible displays!

---

[28] Jeff Goldberg, *Anatomy of a Scientific Discovery* (N.Y.: Bantam Books, 1988), p. 211.

HAS GOD BEEN TOPPLED?

Jerry Adler, a science writer, reviews world class evolutionary thinker Stephen Jay Gould's book, *Wonderful Life*, with these words:

> Science, having toppled God the Creator and exalted Man, now wants to raise E. coli and the rest of the seething mass of terrestrial life up there alongside him. This view does not deny the uniqueness of Homo sapiens and its distinctive contribution to life, human consciousness. It asserts, however, that there is nothing inherent in the laws of nature that directed evolution toward the production of human beings. There is nothing predestined about our current pre-eminence among large terrestrial fauna; we are the product of a whole series of contingent events in the history of our planet, any one of which could have been reversed to give rise to a different outcome.
>
> We are, in short, like every other creature that ever walked or slithered across the earth, an accident....
>
> The survivors...were lucky.
>
> The story of life is one of periodic mass extinctions, which wiped out the majority of species on earth.[29]

Gould, an atheist, and Adler evidently believe that God has been "toppled," that science and man are exalted, and all of this is based on the "lucky survivors" of mass extinctions. So, evolution appears to be based upon death. Because of the death of the "unfit," the "fittest" survive. How might a scientist describe "unfit" life? Do evolutionists believe there is "unfit" life among us today? Did Hitler believe that? Hitler was an evolutionist and apparently thought he was speeding up the process of survival of the fittest. Evolution is not amoral. It is not neutral thinking. It promotes a value system that permits each individual to do what is right in his own eyes.

Evolutionary thought encourages school curricular materials that force young minds to choose who is fit to

---

[29] Jerry Adler, *Newsweek*, November 20, 1989, p. 68.

survive, and who is unfit; who will be rescued in the lifeboat, and who will be left to die of exposure or drowning. No one but God is qualified to describe a certain life as fit or "unfit." Evolutionary thinking wrongly promotes man to the status of God. **"And ye shall be as gods"** (Genesis 3:5b) was part of the four-fold deception offered to Eve by the satanically controlled serpent in the Garden of Eden! Atheistic evolution is the foundation of the deceptive worldviews so prevalent in our day. It forces people to make decisions (for instance about life and death, abortion, euthanasia, and infanticide) that should remain with God alone. The God of the Bible says he knows how many days are ordained for each of us (Psalm 139:16), He knew all about us before he created us in our mother's womb (Jeremiah 2:5, Job 33:4, Isaiah 44:2) and He is the one who ordains our life (Numbers 24:23). Our times are in His hands (Psalm 31:14,15).

WE SEE DEATH AND EXTINCTION, NOT EVOLUTION

Scientists are correct when they observe and publish the fact that mass extinctions have occurred in the past. In the present, extinctions are occurring on a daily basis. What science can prove with facts is that life is disappearing. Life of a wide variety of kinds of plants and animals is becoming extinct. Does this prove that new life forms are now evolving or ever did evolve? *Science has conclusively proven that life is dying and the universe is running down (entropy in action). The fossils are a record of death and extinction. The "Cambrian Explosion"* [30] *is not an explosion of early life. It*

---

[30] Geologists tell us that Cambrian rocks are the oldest rocks that contain numerous life-forms as fossils. Many of these rocks display extremely complex creatures that supposedly existed 600,000,000 years ago. Because there are so many types and numbers of fossil creatures, they are referred to as the "Cambrian Explosion of Life." The Genesis flood is a scientifically feasible explanation for this massive and rapid destruction of living creatures. This universal flood occurred about 4,500 years ago, not 600,000,000!

is a fossil record of the death of millions of complex organisms that, for the most part, no longer exist. The Cambrian Explosion of Life would better be called the Cambrian Explosion of Death! So, therefore, when we look at nature, we do not see emerging new life forms but rather death and extinction—entropy in action!

Carl Sagan used to teach that our sun overcame entropy, thus providing the energy necessary for evolution to happen. Evolution needs more than energy to progress. Raw energy will evolve absolutely nothing without a plan (design) and a factory to direct the energy. So then, if mindless, purposeless, random accidents were to evolve into a life form by using the sun's energy at least three things would be required: Energy, design and an ordering mechanism (factory). In evolutionary dogma, which is absolutely a mindless, totally random chance process, where does a design come from? And who builds the factory to convert the sun's energy into life forms? Sunlight alone cannot cause dead chemicals to evolve into life!

JESUS CHRIST IS THE SOURCE OF LIFE!

The Creator-God of the Bible is the source of life. Jesus said,

> Verily, verily, I say unto you, He that heareth my word, and believeth on him that sent me, hath everlasting life, and shall not come into condemnation; but is passed from death unto life.
>
> Verily, verily, I say unto you, The hour is coming and now is, when the dead shall hear the voice of the Son of God: and they that hear shall live.
>
> For as the Father hath life in himself; so hath he given to the Son to have life in himself;
>
> And hath given him authority to execute judgment also, because he is the Son of man.
>
> Marvel not at this: for the hour is coming, in which all that are in the graves shall hear his voice,

Has God Been Toppled? reality check

> **And shall come forth; they that have done good, unto the resurrection of life; and they that have done evil, unto the resurrection of damnation (John 5:24-29).**

God created life. He created it beautifully designed and sinless. Death came when the first man, Adam, and his wife, Eve, rebelled against their Creator and sinned. Romans 5:12 states:

> **Wherefore, as by one man sin entered into the world, and death by sin; and so death passed upon all men, for that all have sinned:**

1 Corinthians 15:21 continues this teaching:

> **For since by man came death, by man came also the resurrection of the dead.**

If death came as a result of the sin of Adam, then sin, decay and death were non-existent until the Fall. What is the fossil record? It is a testimony of death. Could we have millions of years of death and fossil "man" leading up to Adam when the Scriptures plainly teach "for by man (referring to Adam) came death?" <u>Fossils are a record of death. Without death, there can be no fossils</u>. Do we believe the Bible or do we believe the speculations of scientists? Scientists believe death began millions of years before man evolved onto the scene. The Bible records that death began with Adam.

THE BIBLE AND EVOLUTION IN CONFLICT

As God's creatures, we do not subject the Bible to science; we subject "science" to the Bible. The challenge whether to believe God and His Word or to believe theoretical evolutionary science is presented by Scott Huse, a Christian thinker, in his excellent book, *The Collapse of Evolution*. The conflict of evolutionary theory against the Holy Scripture is impossible to reconcile. Huse lists 24 contrasts between the Bible and evolutionary thinking:

1. **Bible:** God is the Creator of all things (Gen. 1).
   Evolution: Natural chance processes can account for the existence of all things.

2. **Bible:** World created in six literal days (Gen. 1).
   Evolution: World evolved over aeons.

3. **Bible:** Creation is completed (Gen. 2:3).
   Evolution: Creative processes continuing.

4. **Bible:** Ocean before land (Gen. 1:2).
   Evolution: Land before oceans.

5. **Bible:** Atmosphere between two hydrospheres (Gen. 1:7).
   Evolution: Contiguous atmosphere and hydrosphere.

6. **Bible:** First life on land (Gen. 1:11).
   Evolution: Life began in the oceans.

7. **Bible:** First life was land plants (Gen. 1:11).
   Evolution: Marine organisms evolved first.

8. **Bible:** Earth before sun and stars (Gen. 1:14-19).
   Evolution: Sun and stars before earth.

9. **Bible:** Fruit trees before fishes (Gen. 1:11).
   Evolution: Fishes before fruit trees.

10. **Bible:** All stars made on the fourth day (Gen. 1:16).
    Evolution: Stars evolved at various times.

11. **Bible:** Birds and fishes created on the fifth day (Gen. 1:20, 21).
    Evolution: Fishes evolved hundreds of millions of years before birds appeared.

12. **Bible:** Birds before insects (Gen. 1:20, 21).
    Evolution: Insects before birds.

13. **Bible:** Whales before reptiles (Gen. 1:20-31).
    Evolution: Reptiles before whales.

14. **Bible:** Birds before reptiles (Gen. 1:20-31).
    Evolution: Reptiles before birds.

15. **Bible:** Man before rain (Gen. 2:5).
    Evolution: Rain before man.

16. **Bible:** Man before woman (Gen. 2:21-22).
    Evolution: Woman before man (by genetics).

17. **Bible:** Light before the sun (Gen. 1:3-19).
    Evolution: Sun before any light.

18. **Bible:** Plants before the sun (Gen. 1:11-19).
    Evolution: Sun before any plants.

19. **Bible:** Abundance and variety of marine life all at once (Gen. 1:20, 21).
    Evolution: Marine life gradually developed from a primitive organic blob.

20. **Bible:** Man's body from the dust of the earth (Gen. 2:7)
    Evolution: Man evolved from monkeys.

21. **Bible:** Man exercised dominion over all organisms (Gen. 1:28).
    Evolution: Most organisms extinct before man existed.

22. **Bible:** Man originally a vegetarian (Gen. 1:29).
    Evolution: Man originally a meat eater.

23. **Bible:** Fixed and distinct kinds (Gen. 1:11, 12, 21, 24, 25; 1 Cor. 15:38- 39).
    Evolution: Life forms in a continual state of flux.

24. **Bible:** Man's sin the cause of death (Rom. 5:12).
    Evolution: Struggle and death existent long before the evolution of man.

In addition to these specific direct contradictions, there are stark differences of general principle between atheistic evolution and biblical Christianity. Jesus said:

A good tree cannot bring forth evil fruit, neither can a corrupt tree bring forth good fruit (Matthew 7:18 KJV).

The fruit of evolution has been all sorts of anti-Christian systems of belief and practice. It has served as an intellectual basis for Hitler's nazism and Marx's communism. It has prompted apostasy, atheism, secular humanism and libertinism, as well as establishing a basis for ethical relativism, which has spread through our society like a cancer. The mind and general welfare of mankind has suffered greatly as a result of this naturalistic philosophy.

According to the Bible, man is a responsible creature. One day he will give an account for his life's actions and motives. But when man is viewed as the product of some vague purposeless evolutionary process, he is conveniently freed from all moral obligations and responsibility. After all, he is merely an accident of nature, an intelligent animal at best.[31]

Evolution or creation: you cannot have both! Scott Huse's list is brutally clear. Look again at #14, for example. The Bible says in Genesis 1:20-31 that birds came on the fifth day and reptiles on the sixth day. That means birds came before reptiles. Yet evolution teaches as fact that reptiles came before birds. The two views are mutually exclusive. You either believe the Bible or you believe the speculations of men.

Evolution claims that the earth began as a dry planet. Over many years, volcanic activity and comets crashing into earth generated our oceans. This is not what the Bible says. God says earth began completely covered with water. **"And the earth was without form, and void; and darkness was upon the face of the deep. And the Spirit of God moved upon the face of the waters"** (Genesis 1:2). Evolution claims earth started dry. God says it started wet. If you are a theistic evolutionist or a progressive creationist and still hold to Big Bang cosmology, you have a big problem here: Big Bang says dry, God says wet!

Someone might complain about Huse's twenty-four items. For example, #13 might better read, "Whales contemporary with reptiles." Even so, evolution has whales coming on the scene long after the age of the dinosaurs. Most recently some evolutionists are proposing that whales evolved

---

[31] Scott Huse, *The Collapse of Evolution* (Grand Rapids: Baker Book House, 1983), pp. 122-124.

from cows or hippos or wolf-like creatures that "returned to their evolutionary roots in the sea."

WHALES EVOLVED FROM LAND MAMMALS?

The evolution of whales from land mammals (of course from our perspective it never happened) is quite a problem for the evolutionist to solve. As evolutionist Georges Fichter laments, it is "a bit of a mystery."

> Cetaceans [whales] developed from mammals that lived on land, their return to the sea commencing perhaps 60 million years ago. Fossil evidence is scarce, and so the precise and complete picture of cetacean evolution remains a bit of a mystery.[32]

Douglas Chadwick cuts about ten million years off Fichter's numbers by talking about "...a sperm whale, one of 83 cetacean species whose past is firmly rooted on land. About 50 million years ago its ancestors first learned to swim."[33]

It appears that cows and hippos and wolves are still cows and hippos and wolves. And they know how to swim in fresh or salt water from the moment of birth.

One of the supposed transitional forms is called Ambulocetus. Part of a skeleton remains. This creature is published to have been about seven feet long (not enough vertebrae to tell for sure SINCE MOST OF THE VERTEBRAE HAVE NEVER BEEN FOUND!). It is often pictured with four legs and a furry coat. The fur would seem to eliminate the hippo as its ancestor although fur is just an artist's idea since bones do not have fur! Since the pelvic girdle is missing there is no way to determine if the creature

---

[32] Georges Fichter, *Whales and other Marine Animals* (New York: Golden Press), 1990, p.8.

[33] Douglas H. Chadwick, "Evolution of Whales," *National Geographic*, November 2001, p. 64.

walked or swam. [For more about Ambulocetus, see: www.answersingenesis.org/docs/1344.asp]

Related to Ambulocetus is supposed to be Basilosaurus. But Basilosaurus is serpentine and about 70 feet long and fully aquatic. Next is Pakicetus. "...Pakicetus is known only from some cheek teeth and fragments of the skull and lower jaw, so we have no way of knowing if its locomotion was transitional."[34] Evolutionists have in no way proven that whales evolved from land mammals such as cows or hippos or wolves!

ATMOSPHERE BETWEEN TWO HYDROSPHERES?

Huse mentions an atmosphere between two hydrospheres. The water canopy beneath the ozone layer and above where the birds fly will be discussed later (and the canopy is out of favor, even in some creationist circles). But if there was no water above our atmosphere then there would have been rain and floods from Adam to Noah and the rainbow loses its covenantal significance!

Will you bow to evolutionary "science," or will you bow to your Creator? There are certain things in life that are black and white. We should have the integrity, especially as professing Christians, to choose God's Word and not the speculations of men. We Christians need to get off the fence. **"Choose you this day whom ye will serve"** (Joshua 24:15). Will we compromise and serve the gods of evolution or stand tall and stand firm **"against the wiles of the devil"** (Ephesians 6:11b).

You cannot be an evolutionist and believe the Bible as it is written. The plain word of Scripture is "God created." Therefore, evolution of molecules-to-man or wolves-to-whales is a false speculation of man. Walter Brown reveals 57

---

[34] See: Jonathan Sarfati, *Refuting Evolution* (Brisbane: Answers in Genesis, 1999), p. 76.

irreconcilable differences between the Bible and "theistic" evolution in his book, *In the Beginning* [The Center for Scientific Creation, 5612 N. 20th Place, Phoenix, AZ 85016, 1989, pp. 110-115].

MICRO VERSUS MACRO EVOLUTION

When speaking of evolution as a false speculation, we mean macroevolution—one cell to man. What scientists call microevolution, obviously occurs. Microevolution might be defined as genetic variation, but a better definition is "random errors in the genes" within a certain kind of organism. New species can occur within, but not out of God's created "kinds." For example, people are all different even though we come from one set of parents (Adam and Eve, then Noah and the Mrs.). How can five billion plus people vary so widely in appearance and abilities if we all come from the same set of parents? This is adaptation or, preferably, genetic variation, or perhaps, genetic drift. It is not any type of evolution in the sense of changes in the genes.

Microevolution is random changes (errors) in the genetic makeup of an organism. An example might be a bird born with a missing wing on one side or a cat with no whiskers. Microevolution is almost always harmful or neutral to a life-form.

Macroevolution is something becoming something else due to changes that produce NEW information in the genes— such as a cold-blooded reptile becomes a warm-blooded bird or a fish becomes an amphibian or oats become corn.

We have different species of corn, dogs and mustard, but they are still identified as corn, dogs and mustard. There is popcorn, sweet corn, and field corn; hounds, poodles and collies; many varieties of mustard. This does not prove evolution to be true. It only displays the vast amount of original, God-designed genetic information within the families of corn, dogs, and mustard.

Researchers using their intelligence, computers, and sophisticated laboratory equipment can genetically engineer, for example, corn. Perhaps microevolution is a term that could be used to describe what changed the corn, but it was not a random, accidental process. This genetically altered corn may be less susceptible to a certain fungus out in the field, which is good for corn producers, but questions are being raised about whether the corn might not be healthy for people to eat.

DIFFERENT KINDS OF PEOPLE

How might a creationist explain all the different varieties of people? God's record of the Tower of Babel incident in Genesis 11 provides the answer:

> And the whole earth was of one language, and of one speech.
>
> And it came to pass, as they journeyed from the east, that they found a plain in the land of Shinar; and they dwelt there.
>
> And they said one to another, "Come, let us make brick, and burn them thoroughly. And they had brick for stone, and slime had they for mortar.
>
> And they said, "Come, let us build us a city and a tower, whose top may reach unto heaven; and let us make us a name, lest we be scattered abroad upon the face of the whole earth.
>
> And the Lord came down to see the city and the tower, which the children of men builded.
>
> And the Lord said, Behold, the people is one, and they have all one language; and this they begin to do: and now nothing will be restrained from them, which they have imagined to do.
>
> Come, let us go down, and there confound their language, that they may not understand one another's speech.

So the Lord scattered them abroad from thence upon the face of all the earth: and they left off to build the city.

Therefore is the name of it called Babel; because the Lord did there confound the language of all the earth: and from thence did the Lord scatter them abroad upon the face of all the earth (Genesis 11:1-9).

In the beginning, everyone spoke the same language. Therefore, they were able to pool their intellectual resources. Everyone could talk to everyone else. As a result, nothing was "impossible for them" or "restrained from them" (Genesis 11:6). They chose to violate God's command to scatter across the earth (Genesis 9:1), a violation that resulted in God creating the different basic languages. Have you ever thought about the amazing miracle that our Lord performed at Babel? He not only created fully formed languages, but also, before he could instantly program every person on earth with newly created languages, He had to highlight and delete from their brains their old language! And then He put all their memories back into each person's brain in their new language! Husbands still knew who their wives and children were and they remembered how to build, cook, hunt, etc. Oh, the wisdom, genius and power of the God of the Bible!

From Babel onward, only small populations of people isolated from other people groups could communicate with each other. This would explain the "Cave Man" period (see Job 30) as language restrictions and the chaos of the "scattering period" could certainly create some extremely isolated and primitive pockets of people. The language restrictions forced them to disperse across the earth and "in-breed" with relatives. Certain types of people emerged after several generations of this inbreeding. [(God eventually proclaimed inbreeding to be sin and incest in the Law of Moses. Cain and Seth took wives from among their sisters or cousins but this was not sin until the Law came.

> **Ye shall therefore keep my statutes, and my judgments: which if a man do, he shall live in them: I am the Lord.**
>
> **None of you shall approach to any that is near of kin to him, to uncover their nakedness: I am the Lord.**
>
> **The nakedness of thy father, or the nakedness of thy mother, shalt thou not uncover: she is thy mother; thou shalt not uncover her nakedness.**
>
> **The nakedness of thy father's wife shalt thou not uncover: it is thy father's nakedness.**
>
> **The nakedness of thy sister, the daughter of thy father, or daughter of thy mother, whether she be born at home, or born abroad, even their nakedness thou shalt not uncover...(Leviticus 18:5ff).]**

Scientists tell us that all the races of mankind came from a single, female parent. On this point, scripture does not negate "science." Eve is the mother of the race of Adam of which we all are members. The different types of humans (variations within the human "kind") are most probably a result of the scattering of people around the globe by God after the Tower of Babel.

LANGUAGES DON'T BEGIN WITH GRUNTS

The study of language has developed into a complex field of scholarship. Linguists tell us that languages get more and more complex the farther back they trace them. The older ("more primitive") a language is, the more complex it appears to be. This is powerful evidence against evolution.

If evolution is true and man gradually evolved from more primitive creatures, language should get more and more simple the older it is said to be. Prehistoric man should have communicated first with grunts; then with single syllables; then with multi-syllabic words (ba-na-na); then, with sentence fragments, developing into sentences ("I want banana"), etc. What is found is just the opposite. Early languages such as Sumerian are so complex that only a handful of the most brilliant scholars can decipher them. The Tower of Babel incident explains the "races" and the problem of complex "primitive" languages. God created the languages instantly and fully mature. Evolution offers no good explanation for the complexity of the earliest known languages!

THE BEGINNING OF ENGLISH

Linguistic researchers from around the world have published their ideas concerning the geographic location of the "root" of English. Linguists call this language Proto-Indo-European. Two Russian linguistic experts, Thomas Gamkrelidze and Vyacheslav Ivanov, have offered evidence "...that Indo-European originated in an area known as Anatolia, which is now part of Turkey, and from there spread throughout Europe and the sub-continent." (See *U.S. News and World Report*, Nov. 5, 1990, page 62.)

U.S. News and World Report was not the first publication to report that language can be traced back to Turkey. The Bible records for us that Noah and his family had their post-flood beginnings and first post-flood conversations in Turkey:

> **And the ark rested in the seventh month, on the seventeenth day of the month, upon the mountains of Ararat (Genesis 8:4).**

Scientists trace language back to a particular place on earth; the Bible would describe that place to be the mountains of Ararat in Turkey. The linguists agree! Of course, there are other language groups on earth that someone might claim had their origin in Australia or the Amazon thousands of years ago. Your ideas about the origin of language are determined by your "worldview glasses." If Noah and his family were the first people talking on planet earth after the global flood, and the Bible teaches nothing else, then all languages will sooner or later be traced back to Noah or to the Tower of Babel incident.

BABEL AND HI-TECH SCIENCE

Since the creation of languages at the Tower of Babel, the endeavors of generations of mankind have been limited (not able to do the impossible) by the language barrier. But now, for the first time since the Tower of Babel, our generation has a common international language—the language of hi-tech computers. With computers, we can again pool our international research and knowledge and do the impossible (man on the moon, heart transplants, Concorde jet travel, etc.). God stepped into time to stop this situation in Genesis 11:5-7:

> **And the Lord came down to see the city and the tower, which the children of men builded. And the Lord said, Behold, the people is one, and they have all one language; and this they begin to do: and now nothing will be restrained from them, which they have imagined to do. Come, let us go down, and there confound their language, that they may not understand one another's speech.**

Again mankind has a common language. If God stopped one generation from doing what they "imagined," what might He do in our generation? The imagined ideas of evolution are convincing more and more people that God did not make us and is not necessary for any part of our existence. We are rapidly becoming a people who believe the bottom line of William Henley's poem *Invictus*: "I am the master of my fate, I am the captain of my soul." This was the attitude of Babylon, and the Creator was not pleased.

One other thought to consider in Genesis 11—could the people of Babel have been building a waterproof tower? The biblical text states the use of specially fired bricks (hardened) and the use of waterproof tar ("slime" KJV) for mortar. The flood judgment of Noah's day would have been fresh on the minds of these people. Could they have been shaking their fists at God (rebelling) with their pooled intellectual resources as they built a waterproof tower, thus making a statement? "God, you can't get us again with a flood! We will all come together in our waterproof tower that reaches into the sky. We will save our own lives in spite of You. We will control our destiny. We will take charge of our lives." How much of this attitude is like Lucifer—**"I will be like the Most High"** (Isaiah 14:13,14)?

The science of that day may have convinced the people that they could quite satisfactorily live apart from their Creator. Scientists today climb into their ivory towers and say in their hearts and in their papers: "There is no God. We can do quite well without Him. We are all gods and control our own destiny. Evolution has proven that we can be here without the necessity of God." Unfortunately, politically correct thinking has infected the church. Each of us must **"Keep thy heart with all diligence"** (Proverbs 4:23) and not become compromised, neutralized and diluted with the ways of the world. Truly there is a way that seems right, but it ends in death (Proverbs 14:12).

EVOLUTION
AND THE SCIENTIFIC METHOD

Scientists often make proclamations and publish papers that elevate them to god-like status. Are we forced to believe that science and the scientific method have "toppled" God? From our earliest school days, we are taught that science is based on careful experimentation, observation, and disciplined thought. Science gives us facts. We can trust it. We are further educated by television programs and interviews with Ph.D.s like Carl Sagan stating that "evolution is no longer a theory, but a proven fact." This is not the

<u>scientific method</u>! Evolutionist, Hy Ruchlis, defines the scientific method:

> The Scientific Method is the basic set of procedures that scientists use for obtaining new knowledge about the universe in which we live.[35]

Making a proclamation that evolution is no longer a theory, but a proven fact is just that—a proclamation. It is not testable science. It does not fit within the definition of the Scientific Method. Scientific method begins with making an observation. Then, prior knowledge is consulted about your observation and a hypothesis is formed (the hypothesis is some kind of prediction you make about your observation). Once you arrive at your hypothesis, you design an experiment, collect whatever information (data) you can from the results of your experiment and then attempt to interpret your data (results). At this point you again consult prior knowledge and then form your conclusions about your experiment. Ruchlis continues:

> <u>Unless the teachings of the authorities on a subject are based upon scientific method, error can be just as easily transmitted as fact...</u>
> The most important point to remember about the method of science is that it rests upon the attitude of open mind. In accordance with this attitude, one has the right to question any accepted fact. One who searches for truth has to learn to question deeply the things that are generally accepted as being obviously true (Emphasis added).[36]

How does evolution as a "scientific" explanation for origins measure up under Ruchlis' explanation of scientific method? It receives a failing grade. Could evolution be "error...transmitted as fact?" It certainly could. Do

---

[35] Hy Ruchlis, *Discovering Scientific Method* (N.Y.: Harper & Row, 1963), p. 7.

[36] Ibid., Ruchlis, pp. 7,8.

evolutionists present an "open mind?" Do they permit their classroom students to question evolution as perhaps not being "...obviously true?" On the contrary, evolutionists have amply demonstrated they want only one view taught in the classrooms of the world. When a credentialed scientist who is a creationist presents hard evidence to support the Creator and His creation, he or she is accused of teaching religion.

But evolution from one cell to man is not based on the scientific method [37] and is therefore a faith system. That means it is just as "religious" as belief in special creation. The question is not, "Are evolution, science and creation religions?" but "which system of belief—creation or evolution—has the most factual science to back it up?" For example, evolution offers no experimentally verifiable explanation for the origin of matter. There is also no scientific explanation for the origin of life. No doubt about it, Creation and Evolution are both religious faith systems when talking about origins.

MACROEVOLUTION IS NOT TESTABLE

David E. Green (Institute for Enzyme Research, University of Wisconsin, Madison) and Robert F. Goldberger (National Institutes of Health, Bethesda, Maryland) have studied the scientific method and its relationship to the processes of evolution. Their studied opinion is that macroevolution is beyond the range of "testable hypothesis." In other words, it is not able to be proven factually true with the scientific method.

---

[37] "The open mind is one important aspect of the scientific attitude which lies at the base of scientific method. A person who approaches a problem with a closed mind, unwilling to examine new facts, without any desire to make careful observations, and subject to the tyranny of certainty, has little or no chance of solving that problem properly. But a person with scientific attitudes, who knows how easy it is to be wrong, who examines new facts even if they seem to contradict his pet beliefs, who actually goes out hunting for such facts—such a person has a head start along the road to the solution of any problem he faces" (Ibid: Ruchlis, p. 11).

The origin of the first living cell is scientifically "unknowable." In spite of this, evolutionists Green and Goldberger[38] deny the existence of anything supernatural ("paraphysical"). Contrary to the thinking of these two scientists, macroevolution is not science: it is a religion based on faith. Yet religious evolutionists are not willing to let religious creationists present their views in the public school system. In fact, as we all know, our courts here in America ("...the land of the free and the home of the brave.") will not allow an alternative view for the origin of man to be presented in our classrooms without some sort of objection. If creation is so obviously an absurd option for belief, one would certainly have to question why it is such a threatening concept to consider in the classrooms of our children. **Surely, if evolution is true and as easily validated as scientists contend, there should be no threat at all in allowing it to be challenged by the "scientifically absurd" option of creation.**

It is interesting to note that a growing number of evolutionary scientists are realizing that there is a gross lack of scientific evidence to support the molecules-to-man evolution model. The gnawing reality is that, as one evolutionist has stated: "The creationists seem to have the better argument."

---

38 "...the macromolecule-to-cell transition is a jump of fantastic dimensions, which lies beyond the range of testable hypothesis. In this area, all is conjecture. The available facts do not provide a basis for postulating that cells arose on this planet.

This is not to say that some paraphysical forces were at work. We simply wish to point out the fact that there is no scientific evidence. The physicist has learned to avoid trying to specify when time began and when matter was created, except within the framework for frank speculation. The origin of the precursor cell appears to fall into the same category of unknowables" [David E. Green (Institute for Enzyme Research, University of Wisconsin, Madison, U.S.A.) and Robert F. Goldberger (National Institutes of Health, Bethesda, Maryland, U.S.A.), *Molecular Insights into the Living Process* (New York: Academic Press, 1967), pp. 406-407, quoted from *The Quote Book*, p. 20].

THE LORD WILL PREVAIL

When one religion is in competition with another religion, the true religion will ultimately prevail. The God of creation is already the victor. An anonymous writer, M.B., who worked for the Environmental Protection Agency (E.P.A.) expressed it this way:

God created the Heaven and the Earth. Quickly He was faced with a class action suit for failure to file an environmental impact statement. He was granted a temporary permit for the heavenly part of the project, but was stymied with a cease and desist order for the earthly part.

Appearing at the hearing, God was asked why He began His earthly project in the first place. He replied that He just liked to be creative!

Then God said, "Let there be light" and immediately the officials demanded to know how the light would be made. Would there be strip mining? What about thermal pollution? God explained that the light would come from a huge ball of fire. God was granted permission to make light, assuming that no smoke would result from the ball of fire, and to conserve energy, the light would have to be out half of the time. God agreed and said He would call the light "Day" and the darkness, "Night." The officials replied that they were not interested in semantics.

God said, "Let the Earth bring forth green herb and such as may seed." The Environmental Protection Agency agreed so long as native seed was used. Then God said, "Let the waters bring forth the creeping creatures having life; and the fowl that may fly over the Earth." Officials pointed out that this would require the approval of the Game and Fish Commission coordinated with the Heavenly Wildlife Federation and the Audubongelic Society.

Everything was okay until God said He wanted to complete the project in six days. Officials said that it would take at least 100 days to review the application and impact statement. After that there would be a public hearing. Then there would be 10 to 12 months before....

At this point, God created hell!

Evolution may be winning some tactical skirmishes in teamwork with Satan's world system, but let us never forget that our Lord will have the last word. The Creator tells us how everything will conclude in Philippians 2:10,11:

> That at the <u>name of Jesus</u> every knee should bow, of things in heaven, and things in earth, and things under the earth: And that every tongue should confess that Jesus Christ is Lord, to the glory of God the Father (Emphasis added).

Our Lord, our Creator is the Victor! Isaac Asimov, Carl Sagan, Ernst Mayr, and Stephen Jay Gould, as well as that evolutionist college professor or schoolteacher, will all bow down before their Savior and Creator, Jesus Christ the Lord. They will confess out loud with their own tongue, "Jesus Christ is Lord," to the glory of God the Father. They have examined the creation and have willfully chosen to believe a lie. Unless they come to the Lord Jesus in simple faith and confess their sinful rebellion against Him, they will "bow" and "confess" at the judgment to no avail. <u>They will appear at the Judgment before God their Creator without excuse.</u>

> Because that which may be known of God is manifest in them; for God hath shewed it unto them.
> For the invisible things of him from the creation of the world are clearly seen, being understood by the things that are made, even his eternal power and Godhead; so that they are without excuse.
> Because that, when they knew God, they glorified him not as God, neither were thankful; but became vain in their imaginations, and their foolish heart was darkened.
> Professing themselves to be wise, they became fools,
> And changed the glory of the uncorruptible God into an image made like to corruptible man, and to birds and four-footed beasts and creeping things (Romans 1:19-23).

The great evolutionary minds of the day have a tendency to elevate man and creature to the status of God. From chemicals to man, all is essentially equal. "All is One!" But is this wisdom or is it foolishness? God says: **"The fear of the Lord is the beginning of wisdom: And the knowledge of the Holy One is understanding"** (Proverbs 9:10). True wisdom is belief in God the Creator. There is unity and there is diversity in His creation. Man might look like a monkey and even act like a monkey, but he cannot take a blood transfusion from a monkey. As professing Christians, when we fail to bow before God in recognition of His sovereignty and omnipotence, we open ourselves to being tainted with vain philosophies and the foolish speculations of this world system. Have we so devoted ourselves to learning the ways of the world that we have neglected the ways of the Word? Do we stand condemned before our Creator because our true commitment lies with the imaginations and speculations of men rather than with the eternal truths of the Bible? Are we lacking faith because we have drifted into subjecting the Bible to science instead of subjecting "science" to the Bible? Are we seeking the approval of men more than the approval of God (John 12:43)? Truly, **"There is a way which seemeth right unto a man, but the end thereof are the ways of death"** (Proverbs 14:12). "O God, help us with our unbelief!"

MARVEL OF GOD'S CREATION

#3

The Black and Yellow Garden Spider

The black and yellow garden spider is a special creation of the God of the Bible. As does each species of spider, it has its own unique web, which may be spun more than two feet in diameter. At the center of the web, the spider makes a dense area of silk that often gives the appearance of a zipper or zigzag bulk of silk.

The female weaves an egg sac that is pear-shaped and about one inch in diameter. She then hangs the egg sac somewhere close to her main web.

> This spider lays all her eggs at once. There are usually 40 or 50. As each egg is expelled, the female dusts it with a powdery substance. This dusting gives the egg a coating that looks like the bloom on a plum or a grape.
>
> The eggs are enclosed in a silken cup at the center of the sac. The cup, in turn, is covered by a layer of flossy silk. And for additional protection the female weaves another layer of silk around both the cup and the floss. This outer covering is tightly woven and brown in color.
>
> Shortly after the eggs are laid they hatch. The young are known as spiderlings. They break out of the shells by means of an organ known as the "egg tooth." This later disappears.[39]

The black and yellow garden spider is like a miniature manufacturing plant. It produces different kinds of webbing

---

[39] Will Barker, *Winter-Sleeping Wildlife* (New York: Harper and Row, Pubs., 1958), pp. 94- 96.

in more than one color for different purposes, as well as making the powdery substance with which it coats its eggs. Some of its webbing is sticky to entrap insects for food. Other parts of the web are not sticky, enabling the spider to move rapidly across the web without ensnaring itself. How does evolution (the impersonal plus time plus chance) explain the complicated ability of one spider to produce different types of webbing for different purposes and even in different colors (varying from white to brown)? And how does evolution explain the presence of an "egg tooth" in a baby spider?

When the spider decides it is time to move on to new territory, it has an ingenious means of travel:

> To reach new locations the spider travels by a means of transportation known as "ballooning." A spiderling or spider throws out streams of silk. These threads form a sort of "flying carpet." It rises on warm currents of ascending air, and spiders and spiderlings are borne aloft and scattered far and wide.
>
> Sometimes they go as high as 14,000 to 15,000 feet and travel hundreds or even thousands of miles.[40]

Spiders undergo several moults before they are fully grown. If they do not shed their skin, they die. How would the spider know this until it grew too big for its shell and died? Dead spiders do not evolve new abilities!

The skin moults and splits open in a special manner. First, the spider injects a certain liquid called "moulting fluid" between its outer old skin and its newly developing skin. Where does this special fluid come from, and how does the spider know what to do with it and when to use it? Using the moulting fluid too soon or too late is fatal!

The way that the old skin splits is crucial. If it cracks open in the wrong places, or at wrong angles, the spider perishes.

---

[40] Ibid., Barker, p. 96.

Once the old skin is sufficiently loose, splits appear along the sides of the body and in front of the eyes. But no horizontal split occurs across the body. The vertical split along each side of the body and the one crosswise in front of the eyes form a flap of skin.

The spider pushes up the flap like a man thrusting up a hinged trap door. It pushes and pushes and pushes until the flap drops back over the abdomen. Out of the opening wriggles the spider.[41]

What infinite care our Creator-God has taken in the design of the spider! <u>This little creature breaks the rules of the evolution model with its marvelous complexity</u>. It needed God to create it just like it is with all its abilities and peculiarities.

During the summer of 2001, seven garden spiders lived in various places around our house in Texas. As we fed them grasshoppers and crickets (I toss them into the web, but my wife places them in the web), we noticed that they seemed to have different personalities. Most of them would rush out across the web to grab their meal, but one was more cautious. She would wait until the right moment to pounce upon her prey. One day, Jenna Dee placed a large, dead grasshopper in this spider's web. I stayed to see what would happen. The big female spider just watched the lifeless hopper for several minutes. Then she took her two front legs, reached out and tweaked the web. It appeared that she was attempting to shake her web to see if the trapped grasshopper would move. Does a spider think?

Another large female liked to swing on her web. She seemed to notice when we were bringing her something to eat. Several times I walked by her with nothing in my hands and she did not swing. But by the end of the summer almost every time we got close to her with a grasshopper she would

---

[41] Ibid., Barker, p. 97.

start swinging. Could she have been showing her excitement at the prospect of getting a treat? Well, I can't resist sharing one more observation. A third spider had a short trigger. The instant you tossed a bug into her web, she ran and bit it and quickly wrapped it in sheets of webbing. One day I tossed a chlorine-soaked cricket into her web. She ran down and bit it and then jumped back and looked at it like, "What is this? It tastes awful." She then turned around and walked back to her zipper and ignored it. Okay, one more quick one—Another day I put four grasshoppers in the same area of a spider's web. One hour later I came back to see what she had done. To my astonishment, she had placed the four grasshoppers almost exactly twelve inches apart in the form of a perfect square!

The black and yellow garden spider is a marvel of God's creation—the God for whom nothing is impossible (see Luke 1:37; Jeremiah 32:17, 27; Mark 10:27; Matthew 19:26), who daily lives to make intercession for us (Romans 8:34) and who loves us so much that He willingly gave His life for us (John 3:16).

4

"MISSING LINKS" ARE <u>MISSING</u>

A s a college student I was convinced that evolution was true and that, in time, scientists would find the missing pieces. I thought science would ultimately provide us with an unbroken chain of evidence supporting the evolution and relationship of all things. Many scientists are still hoping for this evidence. However, Stephen Jay Gould, former Professor of Geology and Paleontology at Harvard, believes that the unbroken chain of evolutionary evidence will never be found—that what we see in the fossils and in living creatures is more accurately explained with the creation model. Gould was still an evolutionist, but he wrote:

> The birds of Massachusetts and the bugs in my backyard are unambiguous members of species recognized in the same way by all experienced observers.
>
> This notion of species as "natural kinds"...fit splendidly with creationist tenets....
>
> But how could a division of the organic world into discrete entities be justified by an evolutionary theory that proclaimed ceaseless change as the fundamental fact of nature?[42]

Dr. Gould is making a statement about what we see as opposed to what evolution <u>theorizes</u> we ought to be seeing. We see discrete entities, distinct species. In the fossil record, there are fish, turtles and cockroaches. They are individually

---

[42] Stephen Jay Gould, "A Quahog is a Quahog," *Natural History*, Vol. 88 (7), August- September 1979, p. 18.

distinct, identifiable creatures. In life, we can also see fish, turtles and cockroaches. We can identify them. They are not ½ fish and ½ turtle or ½ turtle and ½ cockroach. We do not see elephants evolving fins or whales evolving wings. The discrete entities we see in the fossil record and in life are not "questionable" species. They are not transitional forms, as evolution would require. This is a problem for the evolutionist. If evolution is true, creatures should not be so easily identifiable. Every creature should be difficult to categorize, classify and name, if evolution is correct (and life is "evolving along"). Could it be that evolution is not correct? That each animal is easily identifiable (as giraffe or beetle or fish or turtle or cockroach) truly does "fit splendidly with creationist tenets." Ceaseless change in the fossils or living plants and animals does not appear to be "...the fundamental fact of nature (Emphasis added)."[43]

GOD CREATED KINDS

God tells us He created each plant and animal after its own kind (Genesis 1:11, 12, 21, 24, 25). Nothing evolved from some lower life form and nothing is presently evolving into a higher life form. From a creationist position, what we see in the fossil record and in life is exactly what we would expect to see. And what should we expect to see with our Biblical worldview glasses on? We should see discreet, identifiable living and fossil forms which are or were fully functional, designed and made according to the wisdom and power of Almighty God the Creator! This is exactly what we see. Each form of life displays the attributes of its own kind of flesh: flesh of fish, flesh of birds, flesh of beasts, flesh of humans, etc. (1 Corinthians 15:39).

The lack of transitional forms in fossil and living entities is why evolutionists have the "missing link" problem,

---

[43] Ibid.

although some deny this. The "missing links" are missing. They are completely absent in the fossil record and in living organisms. They never will be found because the Creator did not create transitional forms between kinds of creatures.

God created each plant and animal after its own kind, therefore, you would not expect to see "missing links." Even the most famous missing link, Archaeopteryx, is no longer considered, by many evolutionists, to be a "link." Years ago, Archaeopteryx was believed to be a link (transitional form) between reptiles and birds. Now it is known to be a bird even in evolutionary circles.[44]

"MISSING LINKS" OR "UNBROKEN TIES"

The evolutionist's propaganda machine constantly barrages us through public TV, magazines and newspapers with broad ambiguities and undocumented claims supporting evolutionary theory. A letter in *The Dallas Morning News* by Drs. Alvin and Joel Taurog of Southwestern Medical School exemplifies this type of propaganda:

> Biological evolution asserts that all living organisms are interrelated by unbroken ties of genealogy. Although referred to as a theory, evolution is as much a fact as anything discovered by science, as well confirmed as the rotation of the planets around the sun or the roundness of the earth. The concept of evolution is central to biology and a massive body of evidence corroborates the evolutionary origin of all living organisms, including humans. While much remains to be learned regarding the mechanisms of evolution, the evolution of species is accepted by biologists as proven fact.[45]

Let us evaluate this paragraph of Drs. Taurog. If "...all living organisms are interrelated by unbroken ties of

---

[44] See *The Dallas Morning News*, Science Update, by Matt Crenson, October 23, 1995, and *Nature* of the same month.

[45] Drs. Alvin and Joel Taurog, *The Dallas Morning News*, March 6, 1987, Letters to the Editor.

genealogy," then the leading evolutionary thinker of Harvard, Dr. Stephen Jay Gould, is wrong. Gould states:

> The absence of fossil evidence for intermediary stages between major transitions in organic design, indeed our inability, even in our imagination, to construct functional intermediates in many cases, has been a persistent and nagging problem for gradualistic accounts of evolution.[46]

"Gradualistic evolution" means evolution of one creature into a more sophisticated and more complex creature over long periods of time. One creature gradually becomes another if given enough time. Gradualistic evolution, if true, should have evidence of transitional intermediate life forms in fossils and in living animals. Gould continues:

> All paleontologists know that the fossil record contains precious little in the way of intermediate forms; transitions between major groups are characteristically abrupt.[47]

What Gould is saying is that the missing links remain missing. There are no transitional (in-between) forms. No plant or animal is evolving into a higher form as far as the fossils can confirm. Even in living forms we do not see any chickie-ducks or duckie-chicks!

"SUNRISE" OR "EARTH TURN"

Where are these "unbroken ties" referred to by Drs. Taurog? They present no scientific evidence to support their view. The evidence is only implied. They do appear to erect a "straw- man-creationist" and to take a few sideways swipes at him. In mentioning the "rotation of the planets around the sun or the roundness of the earth" as true science, are they

[46] Stephen Jay Gould, "Is a New and General Theory of Evolution Emerging?" *Paleobiology*, Vol. 6 (1), January, 1980, p. 127, as quoted in *The Quote Book*, p. 8.

[47] Stephen Jay Gould, "The Return of Hopeful Monsters," *Natural History*, Vol. LXXVI (6), June-July, 1977, p. 24. Quoted in *The Quote Book*, p. 8.

implying that the Bible and creationists believe in the "sun rising on a flat earth?" How accurate are these doctors in the use of language? Do they say to a patient, "Did you see the beautiful sunrise this morning?" Or would they be scientifically accurate and ask, "Did you see the beautiful earth turn this morning?"[48] The Bible uses common, ordinary language. That the earth is not flat, but a sphere is taught in Isaiah 40:22: **"It is he that sitteth upon** (above) **the circle of the earth..."** (KJV). The Bible teaches that as God looks down upon earth, it appears as a sphere or circle. Psalm 19 is a scripture that uses normal language and refers to the sun rising. The Bible is not inaccurate because it uses common figures of speech.

Where can we find the "massive body of evidence [that] corroborates the evolutionary origin of all living creatures, including humans," as Drs. Taurog allege? The "massive body of evidence" proving the evolution of man would not fill a single casket according to evolutionist and prolific author Dr. Lyall Watson:

> The fossils that decorate our family tree are so scarce that there are still more scientists than specimens. The remarkable fact is that all the physical evidence we have for human evolution can still be placed, with room to spare, inside a single coffin![49]

Drs. Alvin and Joel Taurog say still more:

> When religion and science come into conflict, it is generally in the realm of belief.... Scientific belief is based solely upon evidence that is validated by observation, experiment and

---

[48] There is another idea called "Geocentricity." It teaches that the earth is stationary and everything else revolves around it. There is apparently no way to conclusively prove either view without stepping outside of our universe to observe how the stars, planets, etc., are moving in relationship to each other.

[49] Dr. Lyall Watson, "The Water People," *Science Digest*, Vol. 90, May 1982, p. 44.

prediction; neither religious belief, nor any other belief system, is subject to these constraints.[50]

Apparently, Drs. Taurog believe that the evolution model of one cell to man is science and thus can be validated with the scientific method. Creation science is apparently religious belief in their view. They add, "The interrelationships among living organisms from microbes to man have never been clearer..." It is not clear precisely what these doctors are referring to, but from the smallest life forms to the largest, from the simplest to the most complex, there is no scientific evidence to prove that they (small to large or simple to complex) are related as ancestors to or progeny from each other. *Natural History*, May 1977, p. 14, published the words of the late Dr. Stephen Jay Gould:

> The extreme rarity of transitional forms in the fossil record persists as the trade secret of paleontology. The evolutionary trees that adorn our textbooks have data only at the tips and nodes of their branches; the rest is inference, however reasonable, not the evidence of fossils... We fancy ourselves as the only true students of life's history, yet to preserve our favored account of evolution by natural selection we view our data as so bad that we never see the very process we profess to study.

CHRISTIANS RAISE THE
WHITE FLAG OF SURRENDER!

Do we Christians realize how much the world's culture has affected us? In the late 1800's, Darwinian evolution became popular. It appeared that the evolutionists had proven the universe to be billions of years old. It seemed so obvious that people came from a monkey-like creature. What did our theologians do? Up came the white flag! They invented theistic evolution in order to squeeze evolution into the Bible.

---

[50] Drs. Alvin and Joel Taurog, *The Dallas Morning News*, March 6, 1987, Letters to the Editor.

In so doing, they subjected the Bible to "science" rather than subjecting "science" to the Bible, and surrendered to the current cultural fad of Darwinism. But we gained the approval of the academicians and intellectuals, didn't we? (See John 5:44; 12:43.)

Now the slow, gradual evolution over millions of years idea is passing out of favor. Dr. Gould has popularized punctuated equilibria, apparently due to the "extreme rarity of transitional forms in the fossil record." Atheist and evolutionist Richard Milton, England's premier evolutionary science journalist writes:

> The difficulty with punctuated equilibrium is that it is wholly speculative and has been introduced simply to account for the lack of fossils that ought to exist in the neo-Darwinist theory.[51]

What are the Christians doing? We are moving with our culture away from Darwinian evolution (theistic evolution is Darwinian evolution with Bible verses tacked on) into punctuated equilibria which we have renamed "Progressive Creation." (Progressive creationism, as far as this writer can discern, is Gould's punctuated equilibria with Bible verses tacked on!) The apparent leader in the progressive creation camp is Hugh Ross. Ross believes that the universe is 16 billion years old and the Flood was a local river overflow. Further, he believes that a soulless race of people roamed the earth before Adam. They lived and died for thousands of years before Adam sinned and God proclaimed death as the penalty for sin! Death before death is an interesting idea.

Both theistic evolution (Christianized Darwinism) and progressive creationism (Christianized punctuated equilibria) demand billions of years of earth history and eliminate the global flood of the days of Noah. Neither of these ideas is

---

[51] Richard Milton, *Shattering the myths of Darwinism* (Rochester, Vermont: Park Street Press), 1997, p.215.

Biblically accurate or acceptable. You see, if the Flood was only 4500 years ago as the Bible teaches, the evolutionists claim there could not yet be all the diversity of animal and plant life—there would not have been enough time for all of these life forms to evolve. So the theistic evolutionists and progressive creationists, following the lead of the pagan evolutionists, hold to the old earth idea. And this is even in spite of evolutionists in their areas of specialty saying the creationists have the better arguments!

MOLECULAR BIOLOGY DISPROVES EVOLUTION

Even at the level of molecules, evidence to support evolution is lacking. In Chapter 2, we discussed the fact that at the cellular level of living creatures there are important differences that distinguish between basic kinds of flesh. For instance, the cells that make up the flesh of birds and fish are not the same. Scientists are studying even smaller entities than cells as they examine the molecules of the cell. This field of study is named Molecular Biology.

A book that every Christian family (and non-Christian, as well) should have is, *Of Pandas and People: The Central Question of Biological Origins*. Written by creationists as a supplemental high school biology textbook supporting the view that life demands a designer, this book deals with the molecular evidence for creation.

> The study of living things on the molecular level is a relatively new field. The information that scientists derive from molecular biology may be used to compare and categorize organisms, a field known as biochemical taxonomy. Biochemical analysis holds out the promise of making taxonomy a more precise science, because it allows differences between various organisms to be quantified and measured....
>
> Proponents of intelligent design read similarity in structure as a reflection of similarity in function. All living organisms must

survive in the same universe and must fit its ecological web. All must fit into a food chain. The need to function within a common universe puts common physical and chemical requirements on all organisms. It would be both logical and efficient for an intelligent agent to design living things with a common biochemical base....

The significant new contribution biochemistry offers is a mathematically quantifiable means of determining how similar classes of organisms are. But when several similarities are put side by side, <u>the pattern that emerges contradicts all expectations based on evolution</u> (Emphasis added).[52]

Animals that evolutionists have always believed to be closely related in the evolutionary chain are now known to be unrelated when studied at the molecular level. Kenyon and Davis continue:

To use classic evolutionary terminology, amphibians are intermediate between fish and the other land-dwelling vertebrates. Yet, analysis of their amino acids does not place amphibians in an intermediate position. This is true no matter what species of amphibian we choose for comparison. Based upon the evolutionary series, we would expect some amphibians to be closer to fish ("primitive" species) and others to be closer to reptiles ("advanced" species). But this is not the case. No matter which species are taken as the basis for comparison, <u>the distance between amphibians and fish, or between amphibians and reptiles, is always the same</u>....

The revolution in molecular biology has given us new, mathematically quantifiable data on the similarities in living things. <u>But the data have served to support a picture of the organic world consistent with the theory of intelligent design</u> (Emphasis added).[53]

Author Michael Denton [*Evolution: A Theory in Crisis* (Harper and Row, 1986)], a Ph.D. in molecular biology (who

---

[52] Percival Davis and Dean H. Kenyon, *Of Pandas and People* (Dallas: Haughton Publishing Co., 1989), pp. 34-36.

[53] Ibid., pp. 37, 38.

is not a creationist as far as I know), argues that evolution from one cell to man is not indicated at the level of the molecule. After looking at molecules for evidence of "missing links" between the different classes of creatures, Denton writes (p. 286):

> There is a total absence of partially inclusive or intermediate classes, and therefore none of the groups traditionally cited by evolutionary biologists as intermediate gives even the slightest hint of a supposedly transitional character.

Of course, if there is no evidence for evolutionary relationships at the level of molecules, which are the basic building blocks of nature, then the idea of evolution of enzymes, proteins, plasma and tissue is totally absurd. The Bible says:

> **For thus saith the Lord, that created the heavens;**
> **God himself that formed the earth and made it;**
> **he hath established it, he created it not in vain,**
> **he formed it to be inhabited:**
> **I am the Lord; and there is none else...**
> **and there is no God else beside me;**
> **a just God and a Savior;**
> **there is none beside me (Isaiah 45:18,21b).**

Dr. Vincent Sarich, an evolutionist and Professor at the University of California at Berkeley, did a series of studies at the molecular level on the evolution of man. At first, his evolutionary colleagues scorned his studies. He had the audacity to announce in 1967 that Ramapithecus (proclaimed by Elwyn Simons and David Pilbeam of Yale to be one of the earliest ancestors of man) was not at all ancestral to man, but more probably an ancestor to the orangutan.

> The year was 1967. Sarich and his partner, Allan Wilson, were comparing blood proteins from human beings, chimpanzees and gorillas—finding them remarkably similar. After analyzing

the slight differences, they decided that the ancestors of human beings must have diverged from those of the African apes only about 5 million years ago, instead of the 20 million to 30 million years that fossil evidence seemed to suggest.

Their conclusion was regarded by many paleontologists as heresy. It was bad enough that Sarich and Wilson were challenging the conventional estimate of the age of the human line. Worse, they were doing it with test tubes and biochemistry—all but ignoring the fossils on which so much evolutionary theory was based. Most experts then believed that human beings could trace their ancestry at least as far back as a 14 million-year-old creature called Ramapithecus, and paleontologist Elwyn Simons, then of Yale, spoke for many of his colleagues when he pronounced the Sarich-Wilson work "impossible to believe."

Times have changed. While Simons still thinks Ramapithecus may be a human ancestor, he has little company. New fossil discoveries have convinced many experts that the animal was ancestral to the orangutan.[54]

Molecular research is eliminating the supposed evolutionary ancestors of people, one by one.

So God created man in his own image, in the image of God created he him; male and female created he them (Genesis 1:27).

---

[54] Kevin McKean, "Preaching the Molecular Gospel," *Discover*, Vol. 4 (7), July 1983, p. 34.

By the word of the Lord were the heavens made; and all the host of them by the breath of his mouth.

He gathered the waters of the sea together as an heap: he layeth up the depth in storehouses.

Let all the earth fear the Lord: let all the inhabitants of the world stand in awe of him.

For he spake, and it was done; he commanded, and it stood fast.

The Lord bringeth the counsel of the heathen to nought: he maketh the devices of the people of none effect.

The counsel of the Lord standeth for ever, the thoughts of his heart to all generations (Psalm 33:6-11).

MARVEL OF GOD'S CREATION

#4

The Gecko Lizard
AND
The Human Ear
(Tiny Things)

These two marvels of God's creation are included not only to display God's incredible designs in His creatures, but also to acquaint you more fully with the type of information you can glean from the creationist magazine, *Creation Ex Nihilo*. In Vol. 14, No. 4 of Sept.-Nov. 1992, two excellent articles appeared that are included here.[55]

Dr. Robert Kofahl teaches us about the gecko lizard on page 6.

A Lizard on Your Ceiling

The gecko lizard can walk across your ceiling upside down without falling off. How does it do this?

Until a few years ago scientists did not know, though they proposed several conflicting theories. Examination of the toe-pads of the gecko with optical microscopes at up to 2,000 diameters magnification revealed thousands of little fibres arranged like the tufts of bristles in a toothbrush. Yet the question remained unanswered. An answer was finally provided by the powerful scanning electron microscope, which was able to take a

---

[55] Robert Kofahl, Ph.D., "A Lizard on Your Ceiling," and Tom Wagner, "Your Hearing: A Powerful Pointer to God's Creation," *Creation Ex Nihilo* magazine, Vol. 14, No. 4 of Sept.-Nov. 1992 (published by Creation Science Foundation Ltd., P.O. Box 302, Sunnybank, QLD, 4109, Australia). In my opinion every family should subscribe to *Creation Ex Nihilo*! [Also subscribe at: www.answersingenesis.org]

series of remarkable photographs magnified to 35,000 diameters and more.

What was revealed?

The gecko has on its toe pads many millions of fine fibres tipped with little suction cups, each about eight millionths of an inch in diameter. In conjunction with this, the lizard's feet are designed so that the tips of the toes bend or curl upward so that he can peel off the suction cups gradually at each step and not get himself too firmly stuck to the surface. It is estimated that the gecko has at least 500 million suction cups on his toes.

The extraordinary microscopic structure of the gecko lizard's toe pads clearly indicates intelligent purposeful design. No remotely plausible scheme for the origin of the gecko's suction cups by random mutations and natural selection has yet been proposed by evolutionary theorists. And should some scientist with a clever imagination succeed in devising such a scheme, he would still be without a scrap of fossil evidence to demonstrate that the hypothetical process of evolution actually took place in the past.

You can't see with the naked eye the tiny suction cups on a gecko's foot. But each chevron-shaped ridge on the gecko's amazing foot pad is composed of millions of fibres tipped with microscopic suction cups. This allows it to walk upside down across your ceiling, or sideways across your wall.

Is it possible that different species of geckos might have different mechanisms on their footpads? The June 8, 2000 issue of *Nature* 405 (6787), pp. 681-685, published an article by Keller Autumn, Ph.D., et al., "Adhesive Force of a Single Gecko Foot Hair." This team of researchers examined the tiny hairs on the foot of the Tokay gecko and arrived at an astounding conclusion: The Tokay gecko utilizes van der Waals forces to adhere to slick surfaces when scurrying upside down across them! Van der Waals forces are weak, short-range bonds between molecules.

Amazing! How would mindless, non-purposeful, totally random-chance evolution produce a foot mechanism such as the Tokay gecko? The utilization of van der Waals forces by a friendly little lizard requires intelligence and engineering much greater than humans have yet exhibited. The foot mechanisms must interact favorably with whatever surface materials they touch (rough or smooth) or the gecko would fall to its death. This little gecko does not use suction cups or a sticky substance. He uses atomic or molecular attraction. With such marvelous evidence of a designer, how can anyone doubt the existence of God?

In the issue of Creation Ex Nihilo referred to above, Tom Wagner composed a "Think Spot" detailing some specifics concerning the human ear (page 13):

Your Hearing: A Powerful Pointer to God's Creation

Contemplation of the size of things that have been created can be a very effective tool in comprehending the greatness of God. For example, consider the Creator's technical ability in a study of human hearing. The ability of our ears to detect sound is much greater than the minimum expected requirement for survival had man simply evolved.

In a book edited by David Lipscomb, 1988, *Hearing Conservation in Industry, Schools, and the Military*, we read on page 303:

'The ear is capable of sensory response to sound whose pressure at the eardrum is no greater than two ten-thousandths of a millionth of barometric pressure. This pressure moves the ear drum about one one-hundred-millionth of an inch. That dimension is approximately one one-hundredth the width of a hydrogen molecule, the tiniest of all known molecules. Therefore, throughout a significant portion of the ear's dynamic range, it is moving in sub-molecular dimensions.'

To visually grasp the incredible sensitivity Lipscomb describes, imagine what it would be like to watch a six-foot man, standing on the surface of the earth, shrink to only one one-hundred-millionth of an inch. The earth, shrinking also—but still enormous when compared to the man—would proportionately reduce to a tiny ball no bigger than the small letter 'o' on this page! The man would become utterly invisible, even to the powerful microscopes of today.

5

ORANGUTANS, MONKEYS AND MAN

When studied at the level of molecules, cells, or fossil bones, the evolutionary ancestors of people (apeman or man-like-apes) are not to be found. In spite of this, elaborate attempts are made to "prove" that man evolved from early primates (ape-like creatures). As one surveys the literature regarding our supposed human evolutionary ancestors, not much agreement is found. A claim by one evolutionist is negated with claims by another.

In the late sixties and early seventies, much of the scientific community ruled Ramapithecus (an ape-like creature) ancestral to the orangutan or to an ape, instead of its original position as ancestral to humans. When considering Ramapithecus in 1973, Alan Walker and Peter Andrews wrote their belief that the jaw of Ramapithecus was that of a true ape (*Nature*, Vol. 244, 1973, p. 313).

Yet, in 1982, the son of Louis and Mary Leakey (world famous pioneers in the study of "prehistoric" man) stated:

> Ramapithecines are thought to be the group from which our ancestors evolved.[56]

---

[56] Richard E. Leakey, *Human Origins*, Lodestar Books (New York: E.P. Dutton, 1982), p. 20. For much information about fossil-man from a creationist perspective please read: *Bones of Contention* by Marvin Lubenow (Baker Books: Grand Rapids, 1992). Also: *The Illustrated Origins Answer Book* by Paul S. Taylor (Eden Productions, P.O. Box 41644 Mesa, AZ 85274-1644, 1992).

PILTDOWN MAN

If Ramapithecus appears in school or college textbooks as part of the evolution of man, it can be discarded, as should the Piltdown Man, which was shown to be a hoax in 1953.[57] Piltdown's filed teeth and bone had been stained to make it appear to be ancient.

Fourteen years after Piltdown Man was proven by the evolutionary scientific community to be a total fake and bad joke, Harvard University Press published these words (admittedly this is a long quote, but I include it to display how far the evolutionary community will go to support their insupportable claims, even years after one of their "evidences" has been proven to be a fraud):

> Unlike all other fossil men is *Eoanthropus*, known from a fragmentary skull and the right half of a lower jaw with two teeth, the first and second molars, in place. The specimens were obtained by Mr. William Dawson from a small opening by the roadside at Piltdown, Sussex, England, and described by Sir Arthur Smith Woodward. It is difficult to determine their age, for fragments of mammals, characteristic of the Pliocene and Pleistocene, are mingled in the river-borne gravel. If contemporaneous with the most modern of them, Piltdown man was probably not more recent than the third interglacial stage, since *Hippopotamus* and other subtropical animals occur with it.
>
> The skull is so fragmentary that those who have studied it have been unable to agree as to the proper reconstruction: estimates of its cranial capacity have varied from 1079 cc. to 1500 cc., and an intermediate figure of about 1300 cc. has finally been reached. It is not at all of the Neanderthal type, but has a high forehead like that of modern man. Aside from the fact that the bones are exceedingly thick, it is not peculiar. The jaw, however, is admitted by all to be more like that of a chimpanzee than like that of any man, living or extinct. This was recognized

---

57 See *The Hominid Gang: Behind the Scenes in the Search for Human Origins* by Delta Willis, with an introduction by Stephen Jay Gould (New York: Viking Press, 1989), p. 24. See also: *The Piltdown Man* by Ronald Millar (New York: St. Martin's Press, 1972), front cover slip.

in the original description. The two teeth are like human molars, but the remainder of the jaw affords too much space to be filled by ordinary teeth. Hence, in his restoration of the anterior part, Smith Woodward made the canines large, like those of a chimpanzee, and allowed for a small diastema. The correctness of his view was demonstrated in a striking way the year after publication, when Dawson and Father Teilhard de Chardin, who were resifting the gravel at the spot where the jaw was found, found a large canine. It is twice as large as that of a man and almost exactly like that of a modern chimpanzee. This association seemed to many to be an unnatural one, so the jaw was attributed by some to a species of chimpanzee. The later finding of a few more fragments at a near-by site seems, however, to have convinced most of those interested that skull and jaw belong together. *Eoanthropus dawsoni* (Piltdown Man) is to some people the missing link between man and the apes. The forehead is high, the brow ridge insignificant, and the brain large, all features of man, but the chinless jaw has the big canines of an ape.[58]

Thus as late as 1967, the prestigious Harvard University Press was still promoting the Piltdown Hoax as a possible "...missing link between man and the apes," when it had been proven a sham nearly fifteen years earlier.

NEBRASKA MAN

Nebraska Man (*Hesperopithecus haroldcookii*) was formed from a single tooth found in 1922. Evolutionist Henry Fairfield Osborn, of the American Museum of Natural History, published in the *Illustrated London News* (June 24, 1922) a picture of a man, a woman and their tools from this one tooth. A few years later, the skull was found and the tooth fit perfectly in the empty socket—it was a pig's tooth![59]

---

[58] Percy E. Raymond, *Prehistoric Life* (Cambridge: Harvard University Press, 1969), pp. 282, 283.

[59] See *The Hominid Gang*, p. 22. See also W. R. Bird, *The Origin of Species Revisited* (Regency: Nashville) Vol. 1, 1991, pp. 227,228.

NEANDERTHAL AND CRO-MAGNON

We might also add that Neanderthal and Cro-Magnon man are now believed to be normal European 'Homo sapiens.' Some of these "prehistoric men" have a larger brain cavity than modern man.

Dr. Percy E. Raymond of Harvard University, states in regard to Neanderthal:

> In actual capacity, the cranial cavity was larger than that of the average European, some skulls measuring 1,600 cc.[60]

Donald Johanson, one of the world's most recognized experts on "fossil man," writes:

> ...Neanderthal Man. He was another Homo. Some think he was the same species as ourselves....
>
> I consider Neanderthal nonspecific with sapiens, with myself. One hears talk about putting him in a business suit and turning him loose in the subway. It is true; one could do it, and he would never be noticed. He was just a little heavier-boned than people of today, more primitive in a few facial features. But he was a man. His brain was as big as modern man's, but shaped in a slightly different way. Could he make change at the subway booth and recognize a token? He certainly could.[61]

According to evolutionist Johanson, Neanderthal is not prehistoric man, not some ancient evolutionary ancestor, but is just like us, modern man! It has also now been proven that Neanderthals made and played musical instruments and that they buried their dead, just like we do!

PEKING MAN

Peking Man has been categorized as Homo erectus. He disappeared during World War II. There is not a single bone

---

[60] Raymond, p. 281.

[61] Donald C. Johanson and Maitland A. Edey, *Lucy: The Beginnings of Humankind* (New York: Simon and Schuster, 1981), p. 20.

left of Peking Man, although books have been written about the international search for the "bones."

An entertaining and readable book on the search for Peking Man was written by Christopher Janus with William Brashler, entitled, *The Search for Peking Man*. Mentioned in the book as one of the people who aided in the discovery of Peking Man is Teilhard De Chardin—one of the perpetrators of the Piltdown Man hoax![62] Since De Chardin was implicated in the Piltdown hoax and managed to involve himself with Peking Man as well, how can we be certain that the documentation we have of Peking man is reliable?

Janus records the total number of Peking Man fossil fragments before the Japanese invasion of China:

> ...they labeled, described, photographed and categorized the casts of the 175 fossil fragments that had been collected.[63]

Peking Man supposedly consisted of:

> ...5 skulls, about 150 jaw fragments and teeth, 9 thigh bones and fragments, 2 upper arm bones, a collar bone, and a wrist bone.[64]

All these bones have disappeared! Apparently, the evolutionary scientists cannot even agree on how many bones represented Peking Man. Johanson records:

> ...5 skulls, 15 smaller pieces of the skull or face, 14 lower jaws and 152 teeth.[65]

So there is no hard evidence that Peking Man is an ancestor of Homo sapiens. Some photographs of Peking skulls remain. The skulls were broken into from the rear and

---

[62] Christopher Janus, *The Search for Peking Man* (New York: MacMillan Pub. Co., Inc., 1975), p. 31.

[63] Ibid., p. 30.

[64] Ibid., p. 32.

[65] Johanson and Edey, p. 34.

most probably, the brains served as food for true Homo sapiens. It would hardly be likely that the ancient ancestor of man lived concurrently with man and that his brains would be considered a delicacy of his great-grandchildren, Homo sapiens. As early as 1957, French paleontologist, Dr. Marcellin Boule, proposed that the people who made the tools that killed Peking Man were true Homo sapiens.[66]

JAVA MAN

Dr. Eugene Dubois discovered a creature in the Homo erectus category, which he called "Java Man." Java Man was a skullcap and leg-bone (Trinil femur). By the end of his life, Dubois recanted. He believed the leg-bone to belong to Homo sapiens and the skullcap to be that of a giant ape or gibbon. Java man was the first of the Homo erectus category. Perhaps a paragraph from Marvin Lubenow's excellent book, *Bones of Contention* (Grand Rapids: Baker Book House, 1992), p.127, would be helpful.

> When people become aware of the massive misrepresentation of the dates for the Homo erectus fossil material, they act perplexed. But the factual evidence is so clear that it cannot successfully be challenged. The perplexity usually gives way to the question, "Why do evolutionists do this?" The answer is obvious. If the date range of all the fossils having Homo erectus morphology were commonly published on a chart as they are in this book, it would be clear that human evolution has not taken place. However, it is possible that evolutionists are not being intentionally deceptive. The reason may be deeper and more complex. Because of evolutionists' faith in and commitment to evolution, I believe we are seeing a psychological phenomenon. Evolutionists give us the dates they want Homo erectus to have, the dates they wish Homo erectus would have. I suspect it is more a case of self-deception on the part of evolutionists than it is an attempt to deceive others. It indicates how deeply their faith has colored their facts (Emphasis mine).

---

[66] Marcellin Boule, *Fossil Men* (Dryden Press, 1957), p. 535.

HEIDELBERG MAN

The other commonly mentioned Homo erectus is Heidelberg Man. Evolutionist Johanson writes:

> Heidelberg Man, for example, was named Homo heidelbergensis. His finder recognized that he was a man and, thus, belonged in the genus Homo, but decided to put him in a species of his own.[67]

Heidelberg Man consists of a single fossil—a lower jaw with teeth.[68] Heidelberg Man is imagination built around a "jawbone!" Some researchers place this fossil jawbone with the Neandertals.

"LUCY" AND THE AUSTRALOPITHECINES

Even Australopithecus is open to question. The star of this "human ancestor" is Donald Johanson's 3½ foot tall "Lucy." Supposedly, Lucy was the first creature to walk on two feet instead of four feet, like other apes did (and still do). Lucy resembles Homo sapiens in three ways (theoretically): her knee, arm-leg length, and left pelvic bone. Except for her human-like knee joint, Lucy's bones resemble the skeleton of an extinct pygmy chimp.

FOSSIL "MAN" SKELETONS ARE COMPOSITES

To be fair to the evolutionists, the fossil skeletons that they put together are almost always composites. In other words, they take a certain area of a country, assume that any bones found there probably came from the same creatures, and then often bring a bone from here and one from there and "compose" a skeleton.

Johanson published Lucy's arm-leg length ratio to be 83.9%. In other words her arm bone was said to be 83.9% as

---

[67] Johanson and Edey, p. 36.

[68] Raymond, p. 280.

long as her leg bone. This would place her about midway between ape (arm and leg of roughly equal length) and human (arm about 75% of leg length). The 83.9% seems quite specific, but the leg-bone had been broken in two or more places and one end was crushed. The pieces do not fit perfectly together, so there is no way to accurately measure it. The 83.9% sounds good, but it is a guess (See *Ex Nihilo*, Vol. 6, 1983, p. 5).

The other human-like bone is the left pelvic bone. This bone is complete and is used to prove Lucy walked upright. The problem is that this bone does not prove upright walking. Johanson believes the bone has been distorted by some means. And yet, there is no other pelvic bone with which to compare it. The bone as it stands, more likely shows Lucy to have walked on all fours!

According to another evolutionist, Dr. Solly Zuckerman, Australopithecus is an ape and walked on all fours like an ape. Zuckerman evaluated the pelvic bone of the Australopithecines and he concluded that this telltale bone corresponded in one type of measurement to monkeys and baboons. Looking at it from another angle, it was "...completely unlike man, and identical with monkeys and apes."[69]

Fellow evolutionist Dr. Charles Oxnard believes Australopithecus walked in a fashion similar to a chimpanzee[70] or an orangutan. Oxnard writes:

---

[69] "It turned out that the angle of twist between the main plane of the ilium and the ischio-pubic part of the innominate in the Australopithecine cast corresponded to that in the four-footed macaque or cercopitheque monkeys and baboons...Another dimension we have examined describes the length of the body of the ischium relative to the innominate as a whole...In this feature, Australopithecus is completely unlike man, and identical with monkeys and apes" [Sir Solly Zuckerman, *Beyond the Ivory Tower* (New York: Taplinger Pub. Co., 1970), pp. 89,91].

[70] Dr. Chas. Oxnard, "Human Fossils: New Views of Old Bones," *American Biology Teacher*, Vol. 41, No. 5 (May 1979), p. 264. Also see: *Fossils, Teeth and Sex — New Perspectives on Human Evolution* (Seattle and London: University of Washington Press, 1987), p. 227.

Let us now return to our original problem: the Australopithecine fossils. I shall not burden you with details of each and every study that we have made but...the information...shows that whereas the conventional wisdom is that the Australopithecine fragments are generally rather similar to humans and when different deviate somewhat towards the condition in African apes, the new studies point to different conclusions. The new investigations suggest that the fossil fragments are usually uniquely different from any living form; when they do have similarities with living species, they are as often as not reminiscent of the orangutan.[71]

Lyall Watson is right. There does not appear to be enough bones from "true" fossil man "...to fill a single coffin." [If fossils interest you, Marvin Lubenow's, *Bones of Contention*, and Dr. Duane Gish's, *The Fossils Still Say No!* are excellent and can be found at most Christian bookstores or at www.icr.org or www.answeresingenesis.org.]

Richard Milton, atheist and evolutionist, says it this way:

In human anthropology, each new fragment of bone or tooth is enthusiastically greeted as further evidence of man's descent by natural selection from an ancestral apelike creature when...every single find of this sort has been definitively assigned to either humans or apes, not to any intermediate category.

This intellectual degeneracy is the outward expression of the fact that neo-Darwinism has ceased to be a scientific theory and has been transformed into an ideology—an overarching belief system that pervades all thinking in the life sciences and beyond.[72]

Milton doesn't pull any punches. He later writes that true science should be open to debate. And that good science is hard work.

---

[71] Ibid., p. 273.

[72] *Shattering the Myths of Darwinism*, p. 240.

Because it is a difficult job, a tacit understanding has arisen that it would be bad form or unseemly to criticize science or scientists seriously, as if they were a banker who added up sums wrongly or a grocer who forgot to deliver the sausages.

I reject this tacit consensus. I am a customer for the scientific service that we pay scientists to provide and I have a customer complaint: I am not satisfied with the answers they have provided on the mechanism of evolution and I want them to go back to their laboratories and investigate further.

I believe it is high time that consumerism finds a voice in the public sector and in the academic world as effectively as it has in industry and commerce. And I do not accept the convention that scientists may be criticized only by their peers.[73]

Just so that there is no mistake as to where Mr. Milton is coming from, permit me to quote him a bit more. His book accuses his fellow evolutionists of having no evidence for their evolutionary claims, especially in relationship to the evolution of man. He says that he experienced a "kind of witch-hunting activity by the Darwinist police" (p. 268) when he published *Shattering the Myths of Darwinism.* Famous Oxford zoologist, Richard Dawkins, described Milton as being "loony," "stupid," and "in need of psychiatric help." Dr. Dawkins went behind Milton's back and wrote, "...letters to newspaper editors alleging that I am a secret creationist and hence not to be believed" (p. 268). Milton continues:

Let me make it unambiguously clear that I am not a creationist, nor do I have any religious beliefs of any kind. I am a professional writer and journalist who specializes in writing about science and technology and who writes about matters that I believe are of public interest.

For anyone, anywhere, to say that I am a creationist, a secret creationist, a "creationist ally," or any other such weasel-word formulation, is an act of intellectual dishonesty by those who have no other answer to the scientific objections I have raised publicly....

---

[73] *Shattering the Myths of Darwinism,* p.276.

> Darwinism still has a large number of critics and it isn't only creationists who have serious doubts about the theory or who have questioned the established view of historical geology.[74]

You have to respect this man! He has more intellectual honesty than a lot of so-called Christians and he has taken a lot of flack for it. But Brothers and sisters in Christ, let us be as courageous in defending the faith! Let us not be intimidated by the wisdom of men. Rather, let us be transformed by the knowledge of God **"The fear of the Lord is the beginning of wisdom: and the knowledge of the holy is understanding"** (Proverbs 9:10).

My dear friend, Mark Cahill, fearless defender of the faith, reminds us of 1 Peter 4:14a: **"If ye be reproached for the name of Christ, happy are ye; for the spirit of glory and of God resteth upon you."**

And then Luke 6:22,23a:

> **Blessed are ye, when men shall hate you, and when they shall separate you from their company, and shall reproach you, and cast out your name as evil, for the son of man's sake. Rejoice in that day, and leap for joy: for, behold, your reward is great in heaven....**

Let us boldly proclaim the Word of God and if we get rejected, let us leap for joy! For the Spirit of glory and of God will rest upon us and great will be our reward in heaven! Hey, my brothers and sisters, when is the last time you got rejected for proclaiming the name and creation works of Jesus. Were you leaping for joy or sad and dejected? Rejection for Jesus' sake brings glory and joy.

ANTHROPOLOGICAL ART

Even the artwork typically used to depict creatures gradually evolving from monkey-likeness to man is

---

[74] *Shattering the Myths of Darwinism*, p. 269.

questionable. Those *National Geographic*-type pictures of apes gradually becoming more and more human until you finally see the man on the street (usually with an ape-like haircut and a beard) are called anthropological art.

> Unfortunately, the vast majority of artists' conceptions are based more on imagination, than evidence.... Much of the reconstruction, however, is guesswork. Bones say nothing about the fleshy parts of the nose, lips or ears. Artists must create something between an ape and a human being: the older a specimen is said to be, the more ape-like they make it.... Hairiness is a matter of pure conjecture.
>
> The guesswork approach often leads to errors.[75]

How did the above words get into an evolutionary magazine like *Science Digest* (now defunct)? Those *National Geographic* pictures of "evolving" man are "artists' conceptions," "imagination," and "guesswork." When is the last time you saw a bone with hair on it? Or how do the artists know what kind of ears or lips to put on skull fragments or even whole skulls? Have you ever seen a bone with a lip on it? As *Science Digest* confesses, it is the artists' "imagination." This is not science!

Every bone or bone particle discovered so far has been classified, by one evolution expert or another, as ape, monkey, or man—not ape-man or man-ape. The evolutionists do not agree with each other as to which fossils prove to be evolving man. It is nice, though, that for the most part, they do not straddle the fence. One researcher's human ancestor is another researcher's orangutan or pygmy chimp. The researchers courageously (and it is courageously) publish their differences while maintaining unwavering faith that an unbroken chain of evidence (proving they evolved from some primate) will one day be found.

---

[75] Author unknown, "Anthropological Art," *Science Digest*, 89 No. 3 (April 1981), p. 44.

IS A MONKEY ALMOST A MAN?

There are other facts to be considered when attempting to prove that man had ape-like evolutionary ancestors. J. W. Klotz lists a few of the important differences between man and the primates.[76] I have edited Dr. Klotz's list of 31 major differences down to the ten most outstanding in my opinion. If man evolved from the primates, then everything in the right column (characteristics of primates) would have to somehow evolve into the characteristics of man in the left column.

MAN	PRIMATE
1. Permanent bipedal locomotion	1. Walks on all fours
2. Great toe in line with other toes	2. Great toe like a thumb
3. Brain larger	3. Brain smaller
4. Head balanced on top of the spinal column	4. Head hinged in front of spinal column
5. Less mature at birth	5. More mature at birth
6. More vertebrae	6. Less vertebrae
7. Shorter arms	7. Longer arms
8. Longer legs	8. Shorter legs
9. One type hand	9. Another type hand
10. 46 chromosomes	10. 48 chromosomes

There are real, basic differences between man and the primates. Let us examine three.

THE GREAT TOE

What would it take to evolve a great toe like that on the foot of a primate into a great toe like one on the foot of a man? This digit on a primate is located and functions like a thumb. With its thumb-like great toe, it can grab onto a tree limb.

And yet the great toe of man comes out the front of his foot in a line with his other toes. In reality, there is no animal

[76] J. W. Klotz, *Genes, Genesis, and Evolution* (St. Louis: Concordia Publishing House, 1972), pp. 332-336.

in the supposed evolutionary family of man with a great toe positioned somewhere between man's "out the front" and primate's "more toward the rear and out the side." There are no living animals and no fossil animals that have yet been found that display a great toe migrating toward the front of the foot. Surely "survival of the fittest" would ensnare and destroy any primate that lost its ability to grab limbs with its "evolving higher" great toe! It would quickly become extinct and would not evolve on up in the "evolutionary chain" to man. Perhaps this is why no fossils have been found of a migrating great toe—any mutation in that direction got eliminated in one generation.

HEAD PLACEMENT

The placement of the head is also quite significant. A human head is balanced on top of the spinal column to facilitate walking and running in the upright, two-legged position. Where is the evidence that the primates somehow managed to move their heads from being hinged in front of the spinal column (for ease of function on all fours) to the top of the spinal column as in humans? How could a creature function, whose head was placed halfway between the primate and man? Obviously, the "survival of the fittest" would catch up with it also. It would probably become extinct in a single evolutionary moment.

BABY HUMANS ARE HELPLESS

Evolution seems to be going in reverse as you look at the ability of human babies to survive, compared to the primates. Human babies are totally helpless at birth and for months afterward. Baby apes are ready to run to safety or climb onto their mother's back for a ride soon after birth. How would those first human babies have survived? And, what is the probability that the last set of ape-parents would give birth to dizygotic twins (a male and female) which could not only survive as the first non-ape human babies, but could reproduce offspring (male and female) which could again reproduce and on and on? And, why do we still have so many species of apes and monkeys, if they are evolving out of something and into something else, perhaps even into people? Again, may I emphasize the fact that what we see over the span of recorded history, in fossils and in real life today, are discrete, identifiable animals, plants and people; not intermediate, transitional life forms.

A MASSIVE POPULATION PROBLEM

If, as evolutionists believe, monkey-like creatures evolved into man about 1 million years ago (Lucy is said to be around 2.8 million years old and some of the more recently discovered "humanoid" or "hominid" bones are said to be much older than Lucy, possibly eliminating her from the evolutionists "tree of human life."), we would anticipate a massive population problem. Dr. Henry Morris gives some interesting figures in his book, *Biblical Cosmology and Modern Science*, published in 1970. Assuming parents lived to the age of 35 and had four children, roughly 3 billion people would have been produced in just the first thousand years! You might say, "Well, that is too many children." Dr. Morris shows the figures for a family with three children, using the same condition as above. In roughly 2000 years, the population of earth would have reached about 4½ billion. With 2.5 children per family and extending the length of a generation to 43 years, in little more than 4 thousand years, 3 billion people would populate the earth. To quote Dr. Morris verbatim: "It begins to be glaringly evident that the human race cannot be very old!"[77]

---

[77] Henry M. Morris, *Biblical Cosmology and Modern Science* (Nutley, New Jersey: Craig Press, 1970), p. 75.

According to Dr. Morris, if the earth's population started with two people 4,300 years ago, it would only have to increase at the rate of 0.5% per year in order to reach the population of the world of 1970. This 0.5% is significantly less than the 1970 population growth rate of about 2% per year. The farther back in history you go, the higher is the percentage of growth. Less industrialized people have bigger families on the average.

Dr. Morris states that the best secular estimate of world population at the time of Christ is 200,000,000 people. Using 2.75 children per family, plus a 40-year generation and starting with two people in 2340 B.C., there would have been about 210 million people alive in A.D. 1. These figures would fit the Biblical time frame nicely.

POPULATION, DISEASE AND WARS

Bringing into consideration the effects of disease and wars on population growth, Dr. Morris says:

> But what about the possibility that the great plagues and wars of the past may have served to keep the population from growing at the indicated rates? Could the population have remained static for long ages and only in modern times have started to expand?
>
> We are unable to answer these questions dogmatically, of course, since population data are unavailable for earlier times....
>
> Furthermore, there is really no evidence that the growth of population has been retarded by wars or disease epidemics. The past century, which has experienced the greatest mushrooming of populations, has also witnessed the most destructive wars in all history, as well as the worst plagues and famines.[78]

Dr. Morris singles out the Jewish people as a good example of the accuracy of his population estimates. The Jewish people had no homeland for many years. They

---

[78] Ibid., p. 76.

suffered persecution and the holocaust. Morris states that if the average Jewish family had 2.4 children and a 43-year generation, after 3,700 years (beginning about the time of the patriarch, Jacob) there should have been 13,900,000 Jewish people alive by 1970.[79] The God of the Bible in Genesis 46:27 says: **"And all the souls of the house of Jacob, which came into Egypt, were three score and ten."** That is a total of 70 family members who came down to live in Egypt. But about 400 years later, at the Exodus, several million descendants crossed the Red Sea on dry ground! Without birth control, abortion, infanticide and euthanasia, populations grow rapidly and exponentially.

Man could not possibly have been here as man for even 1,000,000 years. Using Morris' figures, 1,000,000 years is over 28,600 generations, which would put the world population of 1970 at 10 to the 5,000th power! That is enough people to fill the entire universe, and we are not including rats and rabbits. As Dr. Morris said,

> It begins to be glaringly evident that the human race cannot be very old! ...the assumption of the evolutionists that man first appeared a million or more years ago becomes completely absurd when examined in the light of population statistics.[80]

If man has been recognizable as man for 30 million years, 15 million years or even 500,000 years, there should be hundreds of billions of fossils scattered in huge piles all over the earth! Where is fossil man? Let's face it—man has not been and cannot have been on earth for very much longer than a few thousand years! If studies of population statistics demand a short (few thousand years) history of man on earth, then evolution of man over thousands or millions of years is most unlikely, if not totally impossible!

[79] Ibid., p. 77.

[80] Ibid., pp. 75, 77.

PREHISTORIC MAN IS NOT PREHISTORIC

Could it be that "prehistoric" man was not "before history" after all? Job may have been referring to the type of people scientists call "cavemen" as he wrote:

> But now they that are younger than I have me in derision, whose fathers I would have disdained to have set with the dogs of my flock.
> Yea, whereto might the strength of their hands profit me, in whom old age was perished?
> For want and famine they were solitary; fleeing into the wilderness in former time desolate and waste.
> Who cut up mallows by the bushes, and juniper roots for their meat.
> They were driven forth from among men, (they cried after them as after a thief;)
> To dwell in the cliffs of the valleys, in caves of the earth, and in the rocks.
> Among the bushes they brayed; under the nettles they were gathered together.
> They were children of fools, yea, children of base men: they were viler than the earth (Job 30:1-8).

Perhaps "cavemen" were cast-offs from the civilized societies of their day. Possibly these were people given over to a reprobate mind due to their habitual sin and decadence. In any event, they were not man's ancestors. They lived concurrently with man.

The God of the Bible says He created man after His own image from the dust of the earth:

> And the Lord God formed man of the dust from the ground, and breathed into his nostrils the breath of life; and man became a living soul (Genesis 2:7).

God formed man from dust, not from some prehistoric, ape-like, hominid creature or the primordial ooze. The dust became, by God's creative design and power, a man; but the man had no life until God breathed life into him. Genesis 2:7 clearly shows that man's emergence from some previous living creature is not true. He came from non-living dust, which became, by God's creative design and power, a man— a man that had no life until the living God breathed life into him. This means that man could not have evolved from some more primitive "LIVING" monkey-like creature. People were created by God in God's own image.

Part of God's image is our ability to think thoughts and make decisions. Our brain does not originate thoughts.

> If it did, we would have to do whatever our brains decided. On the contrary, we (the real persons inside) do the thinking and deciding, and our brains take these non-physical thoughts and translate them into physical actions through a connection between the spirit and body that science can't fathom....
>
> Science cannot escape the fact that man himself, like his Creator, must be a nonmaterial being in order to originate the thoughts processed by the brain.[81]

There can be no compromise for the Christian as to the origin of man. We did not come from monkey-like creatures, but through the indescribable, unfathomable, supernatural power of the God of the Bible. He created us in His image, **"unto good works, which God hath before ordained that we should walk in them"** (Ephesians 2:10).

THE ANTHROPIC PRINCIPLE

God placed man, the pinnacle of His creation, in a special environment of delicately balanced systems. Scientists are now calling this balance of ecosystems (that support the life of man) the "Anthropic Principle." For our lives to be maintained, we must have exactly the correct amounts of oxygen, hydrogen, carbon dioxide, sunlight, magnetic field,

---

[81] Dave Hunt, "The Living Word of God," *The Berean Call*, P.O. Box 7019, Bend, Oregon 97708, January 2001.

speed of rotation and revolution of earth, distance from the moon, distance from the sun, ozone, water, gravity, etc., etc., etc. All of these factors must be in the correct amounts, in the right places, at the right times, and in exact relationships with each other.

For instance, if our earth's gravity were weaker, our atmosphere would thin out and would be unable to support life. If gravity were stronger, undesirable gases, such as ammonia gas, would be held in higher concentrations and would be detrimental to life. That means our earth has to have been made exactly the right size to generate the perfect amount of gravity to support our atmosphere.

But the earth also had to be the right size to hold our moon in orbit—that means the moon had to be made the right size so it wouldn't drift off into space or crash into earth—and the moon also had to be the right size so that the ocean tides stay under control. That means there had to be just the right amount of water in the oceans to harmonize with the size of the moon to establish the tidal patterns. Of course, the earth and moon must be in a precise relationship not only with each other but also with our sun, and the size of all three does not leave space for error. How many chance events would have to occur to make all these conditions (and many billions more) just EXACTLY right for man to live on this planet? This requires a lot of faith. We could go on and on with this, but the fact is, the evolution model as an explanation for this incredible universe, so carefully designed with man in mind, is grossly lacking! God, the God of the Bible, is to be praised. He, alone, is to receive the glory and the honor. **"It is a good thing to give thanks unto the Lord, and to sing praises unto thy name, O most High"** (Psalm 92:1).

The heavens declare the glory of God;
  and the firmament sheweth his handiwork.
Day unto day uttereth speech,
  and night unto night sheweth knowledge.
There is no speech nor language,
  where their voice is not heard.
Their line is gone out through all the earth,
  and their words to the end of the world.
  In them hath he set a tabernacle for the sun,
Which is as a bridegroom coming out of his chamber,
  and rejoiceth as a strong man to run a race.
His going forth is from the end of the heaven,
  and his circuit unto the ends of it:
  and there is nothing hid from the heat thereof.
The law of the Lord is perfect, converting the soul:
  the testimony of the Lord is sure, making wise the simple.
The statutes of the Lord are right, rejoicing the heart:
  the commandment of the Lord is pure, enlightening the
  eyes.
The fear of the Lord is clean, enduring forever:
  the judgments of the Lord are true and righteous altogether.
More to be desired are they than gold, yea, than much fine gold:
  sweeter also than honey and the honeycomb.
Moreover by them is thy servant warned:
  and in keeping of them there is great reward.
Who can understand his errors?
  cleanse thou me from secret faults.
Keep back thy servant also from presumptuous sins;
  let them not have dominion over me; then shall I be
  upright, and I shall be innocent from the great
  transgression.
Let the words of my mouth, and the meditation of my heart,
  be acceptable in thy sight, O Lord, my strength, and my
  redeemer (Psalm 19).

MARVEL OF GOD'S CREATION

#5

The Giraffe

Let us look at another of the marvels of God's creation—the giraffe. The giraffe had to be created as a fully functional and unique animal.[82] A mature bull giraffe stands at about 18 feet tall. In order to pump blood up his long, skinny neck to his brain, the giraffe needs a powerful pump. His heart (pump) can be up to 2½ feet long. It is so powerful that, as the animal bends its head down to satisfy its thirst, the blood pressure is more than enough to burst the blood vessels of its brain.

If evolution is true, then the giraffe is back to mindless, totally random accidental chance processes, occurring over long periods of time, to save its life and prevent it from blowing its brains out every time it bends its head down to get a drink of water. This evolution idea comes up short! Is evolution a progressive and miraculously intelligent process that, without a shred of intelligence, somehow realizes that an improvement or adaptation is needed and then sets out to design and manufacture the incredibly complex organic structure? And if the complex improvement does not show up in time, the animal is dead and extinct.

Even the extinct fossil animals have all the necessary parts to exist; they do not display a partially formed skeleton

---

[82] Bob Devine, *God in Creation* (Chicago: Moody Press, 1982), pp. 35-37. This booklet shows how ten different animals (including the giraffe) and plants demand a Creator by their special features.

or fin or beak, etc. All fossil and living forms are fully functional and perfectly suited for their niche.

When might the giraffe know it needed to protect its brain from the devastation of excessive blood pressure? It seems to me that it would not know until it had died of a brain hemorrhage while taking a cool drink. How can it "evolve" a protective mechanism, if it is no longer alive to do it?

The giraffe has a protective mechanism that was designed by our Creator. As the bull bends his head down for a drink, valves in the arteries in its neck begin to close. Blood beyond the last valve continues moving toward the brain. But instead of passing at high speed and pressing into the brain and damaging or destroying it, that last pump is shunted under the brain into a group of vessels similar to a sponge. This cluster of blood vessels is called the "rete mirabile." The brain is preserved as the powerful surge of oxygenated blood gently expands this "sponge" beneath it.

However, from this mechanism another problem arises. A lion creeps up and prepares to kill its spotted prey. The giraffe quickly raises its head and, without something to compensate for the reduced blood flow, passes out. It got up too fast, generating low blood pressure and diminished oxygen content in the brain. The lion eats a hearty meal, and the giraffe, were it alive, would realize that it had better evolve some mechanism to re-oxygenate its oxygen-deprived brain! We all know that animals that have been eaten by a lion don't evolve anything, even though evolutionists would have us believe that creatures evolve the necessary-for-life improvements, as they are needed for survival.

But the giraffe survives! The Creator designed it in such a way that as he begins to raise his head, the arterial valves open. The "sponge" squeezes its oxygenated blood into the brain; the veins going down the neck contain some valves, which close to help level out the blood pressure, and the giraffe can quickly be erect and running without passing out and becoming lion lunch. God made the giraffe just like it is with all systems complete and ready for any emergency. There is no way the giraffe could have evolved its special features slowly and gradually over long periods of time as evolution demands. The functional mechanisms of the giraffe demand God to be their Creator. Why not God as the Creator of everything?

Everyone agrees, creationists and evolutionists—a giraffe is a giraffe. It is a distinct species, a discrete entity. No one would say a giraffe is a "missing link" or a "transitional form." A giraffe is not some creature emerging from some other creature or changing into a "higher" or more complex animal—a giraffe is a giraffe! It can be scientifically examined with results that display the necessity of a single creative act. This long-necked creature had to have been originally formed with all of its complex features fully functional.

Every living organism must be fully functional and perfectly designed for its place in nature or it ceases to exist. Hearts, lungs, intestines, kidneys, brains, blood vessels, nerve pathways, eyes, skin, hair, feathers, scales, teeth, tongues, antlers, horns, reproduction abilities, etc., etc., etc., must all be in place and functioning in harmony or the life form dies! The same is true of cars. They must be designed and produced in such a way that the water pump, carburetor, fuel lines, battery, transmission, ignition switch, etc., are each working properly and in harmony with everything else or the car does not run. Everything must be there and be working from the beginning!

Someone might interject that the giraffe is a product of "survival of the fittest." Let's think about this survival of the fittest idea. Does it support evolution or does it fit creation? Suppose there were two bull giraffes and one female giraffe.

The first bull giraffe is a happy, healthy, 100% bull giraffe. The second bull is evolving out of giraffe-hood so he is not quite fully and completely a giraffe anymore. These two bulls are going to fight, as animals do, to see which one gets the female giraffe. Which bull do you think is the fittest and will win the fight? Obviously the most giraffe-ish giraffe will proudly win the battle and the affection of the female. Survival of the fittest means that the fittest survive. This idea better fits the Biblical teaching that each life form is created according to its kind. The strongest of its kind survives.

The giraffe is a giraffe and it testifies to the existence of its Creator, the Lord Jesus Christ! Have you thought much about the sheer genius of our Creator Lord Jesus? He started with nothing—no patterns or examples—and just thought everything up and everything works! Think of the amazing diversity of plants and animals, not to mention insects that look like nothing else. There is no conceivable possibility for intermediate or transitional forms. He has set apart so many different forms of living things with unbridgeable gaps and a total impossibility of interrelatedness. From snakes, birds, bugs and orchids in all colors, shapes and sizes to fish, cats and giraffes, the unmatchable creative power of the Lord Jesus Christ completely overwhelms the idea of mindless, purposeless, accidental, non-directed chance evolution!

6

THE TEN COMMANDMENTS AND THE DAYS OF THE CREATION WEEK

In 1971, two students had the courage to politely challenge one of their professors (me) to defend his position on the origin of all things. That seemed to be a fairly easy job since I was convinced that huge volumes of factual scientific evidence proved evolution (over billions of years) to be true. By 1972, this professor's stomach was churning with frustration! The evidence for an old universe promoted as proven fact by evolutionists was nowhere to be found. This is not to say that there is lack of writing on the subject of evolution, but that there is no true scientific evidence that is not based on assumptions (refer back to the beginning of Chapter 2, Seven Basic Assumptions).

It was obvious to me back in the early 1970's that evolution needed long periods of time. Couldn't those days of Genesis 1 be a billion years each? If we could somehow impose long periods of time onto the text of Genesis 1, evolution and the Bible quite nicely harmonize with each other. Or so I thought.

24-HOUR DAYS OR AEONS OF TIME?

Those days of Genesis are 24-hour days! If we believe the Bible, they cannot be one billion years each. Even the logic in

135

the Ten Commandments demands 24-hour days [It wouldn't hurt any of us to review the Ten Commandments], so let's make some observations from Exodus 20:1-20:

> And God spake all these words, saying,
>
> I am the Lord thy God, which have brought thee out of the land of Egypt, out of the house of bondage.
>
> Thou shalt have no other gods before me.
>
> Thou shalt not make unto thee any graven image, or any likeness of any thing that is in heaven above, or that is in the earth beneath, or that is in the water under the earth:
>
> Thou shalt not bow down thyself to them, nor serve them: for I the Lord thy God am a jealous God, visiting the iniquity of the fathers upon the children unto the third and fourth generation of them that hate me;
>
> And showing mercy unto thousands of them that love me, and keep my commandments.
>
> Thou shalt not take the name of the Lord thy God in vain; for the Lord will not hold him guiltless that taketh his name in vain.
>
> Remember the sabbath day, to keep it holy.
>
> Six days shalt thou labour, and do all thy work:
>
> But the seventh day is the sabbath of the Lord thy God: in it thou shalt not do any work, thou, nor thy son, nor thy daughter, thy manservant, nor thy maidservant, nor thy cattle, nor thy stranger that is within thy gates:
>
> For in six days, the Lord made heaven and earth, the sea, and all that in them is, and rested the seventh day: wherefore the Lord blessed the sabbath day, and hallowed it.
>
> Honour thy father and thy mother: that thy days may be long upon the land which the Lord thy God giveth thee.
>
> Thou shalt not kill.
>
> Thou shalt not commit adultery.
>
> Thou shalt not steal.
>
> Thou shalt not bear false witness against thy neighbor.
>
> Thou shalt not covet thy neighbour's house, thou shalt not covet thy neighbour's wife, nor his manservant, nor his maidservant, nor his ox, nor his ass, nor any thing that is thy neighbour's.

And all the people saw the thunderings, and the lightnings, and the noise of the trumpet, and the mountain smoking: and when the people saw it, they removed, and stood afar off.

And they said unto Moses, Speak thou with us, and we will hear: but let not God speak with us, lest we die.

And Moses said unto the people, Fear not: for God is come to prove you, and that his fear may be before your faces, that ye sin not.

Did you notice that man's "workweek" is parallel to God's "workweek" (Exodus 20:9-11)? Thus, if man works six 24-hour days, then the logic of Exodus 20:11 requires that God worked six 24-hour days and rested during the seventh day as man is to rest one day a week. The idea here is that God worked the same kind of days that man works. I realize that workdays sometimes feel like they are one billion years long, but we all know that they are not.

An interesting fact of history that might be appropriate to insert here is this: The French, during the French Revolution, attempted to become an atheistic society. They tried to get everything that had to do with the Bible out of French culture, so they went to a ten-day week. Are the French still practicing a ten-day week? Absolutely not! It does not work. There are astronomical events that differentiate days from months and months from years (sunrise and sunset, full moons, spring, summer, fall and winter), but only God's Word and His Creation-week-example point us to the seven-day week.

Hebrew scholars universally agree that the days (the Hebrew word "yom") of Genesis 1 are 24-hour days. These scholars may not necessarily believe that God has the ability to create everything in six normal days, or they may not even believe that the Bible is God's inspired Word, but they do believe the Hebrew word, yom, means 24-hour day.

Liberal scholars have tried to claim that some primitive writer, who had no knowledge of science and geology, wrote down a brief account of the origin of man in overly simplistic terms. Many scholars say that it does not matter what the words say, but simply that it is the meaning or the message behind these "word-symbols" that is important. However, if that is true, then we might as well throw out the Hebrew and Greek lexicons (dictionaries). Every word in Genesis 1 is in the Hebrew lexicon. Every word has a definite meaning and we can look up what that meaning is. It is not some nebulous "word-symbol" that is limited in meaning only by the extent of the imagination of the reader. Today, on the university campuses, this method of madness is called Postmodern Deconstructionism. Naturally, if the true meaning of words is up to you or your professor, then the meaning of the Bible is nonsense.

More than ninety-eight percent of the time that yom (day) is used in the Old Testament (over 2,500 times), it means 24-hour day or the daylight part of a standard day. The rest of the time it refers to such things as the "Day of the Lord," which scholars argue could be anywhere from a 24-hour day to 1,000 plus years to eternity. The fact is that Genesis 1 uses yom with clarifiers such as day one, day two, etc. Everywhere else in the Bible that yom is used with clarifiers (numbers one, two, three, etc.) it unquestionably indicates a 24-hour day.

EACH DAY IS HALF LIGHT
AND HALF DARK

God used every word He possibly could to show us He is referring to one rotation of the earth in front of its source of light (or one revolution of the light source around planet earth which is called Geocentricity). These are 24-hour "yoms" in Genesis 1. He literally says, "...There was evening and there was morning, day one; ...there was evening and there was morning, day two," etc. Each day had an evening and each day had a morning. In Genesis 1:5, God says, **"And God called the light Day and the darkness he called Night. And the evening and the morning were the first day."**

Notice that each day was part light and part darkness. This eliminates theistic evolution and day-age theories, since each day (one billion years?) would be half light and half dark! You cannot evolve anything in 500 million years of darkness or, for that matter, in 500 million-year stretches of unrelenting sunlight.

We might ask, "How old was Adam when he died?" Genesis 5:5 reads: **"And all the days that Adam lived were nine hundred and thirty years: and he died."** If one single Genesis 1 day equals one billion years, as theistic evolution demands, and Adam lived through at least half of day six, all of day seven and 930 more years, then how old was Adam when he died? Was he, let's say, 1 billion 500 million 930 years old? Or did he die at the age of 930? You can't have both! You can't have long periods of time (day-age, theistic evolution, progressive creation) and the Bible. Either Adam was 930 years old when he died, or you can throw out Genesis 1:1 through 5:5!!

DAYS, YEARS AND SEASONS

God had words that He could have used if He had wanted us to understand those days of Genesis, Chapter 1, to be longer than 24 hours. One of these Hebrew words is "olam." Olam means a long period of time and can even mean everlasting. God put all the necessary words into the Hebrew text to make it unmistakably clear to the reader—these are 24-hour days.

Look at Genesis 1:14:

And God said, Let there be lights in the firmament of the heaven to divide the day from the night; and let them be for signs, and for seasons, and for days, and years.

God here differentiates between days and seasons and years. How can anyone stretch a Genesis 1 day into a billion years and then make any sense at all of Genesis 1:14? If a day is a billion years, then how long is a season or a year? Is a Biblical year 365 billion years? Even the most radical evolutionists claim the universe is not much older than twenty billion years! God lines up all these time words for us in one verse to prove that He means 24-hour days. You can't make any sense at all of Genesis 1:14, if you insist on the theistic evolution or day-age or progressive creation views. (Don't forget—we do not subject the Bible to science, we subject science to the Bible.) If "science" tells us we must have long geologic ages to explain the existence of all things, but the Bible says God did it all in six normal days, then we must believe the Bible by faith and know that evolutionary science has some more research to do in its faith system to catch up with the Bible.

The Ten Commandments in the Bible may be one of the root causes for belief in the evolution model. Scientifically credentialed people closely examine God's creation. What they see is the handiwork of God (Romans 1 and Psalm 19), but they nevertheless choose to believe the lie of evolution because they do not want to acknowledge their sin, as recorded in the Ten Commandments. To accept belief in God, who wrote those Ten Commandments with His own finger, becomes unthinkable. Belief would place man in a position of submission and obedience to his Creator, which would never be his choice without the penetrating grace of God.

Furthermore, this position of submission and obedience demands responsibility before this holy God and ultimately, the certainty of judgment—realities that people do not like to think about. We know we are sinners. We cannot even live up to our own standards; let alone, God's righteous standards. It is easier to live in the fantasyland of evolution than in reality when we are separated from our Creator by our own unholiness and pride. Life appears to be less complicated and more comfortable as we believe the lie of evolution. **"The fool has said in his heart, there is no God"** (Psalm 14:1).

No rational person would argue that God's Ten Commandments are invalid or inaccurate or harmful to society. If everyone obeyed them, we would have a near-perfect, crime-free and pollution-free world.

Did you notice that the seven-day creation week is mentioned in the Ten Commandments (Exodus 20:11)? Is this not fascinating? In view of all the many things the Creator could have mentioned to be preserved forever, He chose, in the midst of His Ten Commandments, to call attention to the original seven-day week of creation.

The English translation of the Ten Commandments is accurate. What we read is precisely what God said. He said, **"For in six days the Lord made heaven and earth, the sea and all that in them is..."** (Exodus 20:11). That means exactly what it says. In a literal six days, the Lord made everything that exists, whether it exists in the heavens or on the earth or in the seas. He made it <u>functionally mature</u>. As some might say, it had the <u>appearance of age</u>. That would include the entirety of the macrouniverse (space, time, stars, planets, sun, moon, comets, asteroids, angels, etc.) and the microuniverse (the molecules, atoms and quarks, of elephants, beetles and sharks). A six-day creation leaves no room at all for theistic evolution and its billions of years, or for a "gap" between Genesis 1:1 and 1:2. There was no heaven, earth or sea before the first day of the original seven-day creation week. Only the Trinitarian God of the Bible existed before the first day of that week!

THE "GAP"

Some of the early twentieth century Bible scholars came to believe in a "gap theory" due to the influence of evolutionary "science." These godly men believed that science had established great geologic ages and "prehistoric" man to be a proven fact. They went to the early chapters of Genesis and attempted to subject the Bible to science by postulating a "gap" between Genesis 1:1 and 1:2. But the sun, stars, heat, light, atmosphere and universe were not yet created. No life existed nor could it exist in the supposed "gap" between Genesis 1:1 and 1:2.

There was no "pre-Adamic" race of wicked people living in the "gap." Not only could they have not existed without light, but sin and wickedness, decay and death did not enter the universe until the fall of Adam.

Romans 5:12 teaches:

Wherefore, as by one man (Adam) sin entered into the world, and death by sin; and so death passed upon all men, for that all have sinned.

Before the Fall, everything in God's creation was <u>very</u> <u>good</u>. **"And God saw everything that he had made, and, behold, it was very good. And the evening and the morning were the sixth day"** (Genesis 1:31). Could "very good" from our holy God's perspective include a history of death, suffering and decay in the supposed pre-Adamic fossil record before sin and death entered through Adam's sin? I do not think so. And furthermore, what could God possibly be talking about in Acts 3:18-21 where He states that Jesus will come back to earth to restore all things for times of refreshing? The idea seems to be in Acts that the curse will be removed and an "Edenic" earth will result. If there has always been death, decay and suffering on earth, even before the Fall of Adam, then how could we possibly gain any kind of understanding of Acts 3? Jesus comes back to restore earth to its original pre-Adamic sin death and decay? Not likely!

A sobering result of Adam's sin was death, but before Adam's sin there was no death. If there were no death before Adam (the very clear statement of God's word), then it would be impossible to have "pre-Adamic" people dying.

Actually, the entire creation was affected by Adam's sin and it still "groans" with thorns, thistles and entropy as it awaits its redemption. Romans 8:22-23 states:

> **For we know that the whole creation groaneth and travaileth in pain together until now. And not only they, but ourselves also, which have the firstfruits of the Spirit, even we ourselves groan within ourselves, waiting for the adoption, to wit, the redemption of our body.**

FOSSIL THORNS IN OLD ROCK LAYERS

As a little aside, did you know that thorns are present in some of the oldest sedimentary rock layers? If you hold to a theistic evolution or progressive creation model (old earth) you have a problem here! If thorns are a result of the Fall, and the Fall happened about 6,000 years ago, how can thorns be in rock layers that evolutionists believe are millions of years older than man's appearance on earth? Resulting from Adam's sin God said, **"...cursed is the ground for thy sake; in sorrow shalt thou eat of it all the days of thy life; Thorns also and thistles shall it bring forth to thee..."** (Genesis 3:17b-18a). Thorns came into existence after Adam's sin! So what worldview glasses do you have on? Did thorns come into existence about 6,000 years ago as the Bible teaches, or millions of years ago as evolution teaches?

SOME "GAP" PROBLEMS

Holding to the "gap" position (millions of years between Genesis 1:1 and Genesis 1:2) not only demands death before the Fall, but it also forces changes in the Biblical text. Genesis 1:2 must be changed from **"And the earth was without form**

and void" to "and the earth <u>became</u> without form and void." God uses the very same word for "was" in Genesis 2:25 and 3:1. Genesis 2:25 says, **"And they were both naked...."** Adam and Eve were not created with clothes and then "became" naked.

The same can be said for the serpent in 3:1. It is not that he "became" subtle (crafty, NASB) after not being subtle; he was crafty from the beginning. The Gap theory necessitates changes in other Biblical texts also. For a comprehensive study of problems with the Gap theory please read Dr. John Whitcomb's book, *The Early Earth: Revised Edition* and Dr. Weston W. Fields' book, *Unformed and Unfilled.*

We do not need to accommodate Scripture to what we might believe to be factual science—the geological ages—by imposing a gap between Genesis 1:1 and 1:2 or by stretching the 24-hour days of Genesis 1 into long ages of geologic time. Men, who have done this most probably in all innocence, violate a basic rule: <u>**The Bible must never be subjected to science, but theoretical "science" must always be subjected to the Bible.**</u>

My position, quite frankly, is of one who committed his life to the Lord Jesus Christ later in life than most (age 27) and who endured a gut-wrenching five-year struggle with this issue. When I came to faith in Jesus Christ as my Lord and Savior, I became a theistic evolutionist. I then later saw, as many men and women have seen (when exposed to the <u>true</u> truth of the Bible), the total "rightness" and reality of God's six-day creation that occurred about 6,000 years ago. The true science I studied showed the incredible complexity of every plant, animal and insect. And yet, there was no satisfactory answer to the "why" and "how" of this complexity and diversity—except to say, "all that 'is' results from mindless, purposeless, impersonal, totally random and accidental chance processes plus time." If any causative factor was mentioned, it was always "Mother Nature" did it, but never the personal Creator/Redeemer God of the Bible.

Our God, the Almighty Creator, does not need time. He is above time. The Creator, the Lord Jesus, displayed His supernatural ability to act without time restraints through His miracles. When we believe Genesis 1 as it is written, we bow in worship and in submissive trust of our awesome, infinite Creator. As Job said:

> **I know that Thou canst do every thing, and that no thought can be withholden from thee. I have heard of thee by the hearing of the ear: but now my eye seeth thee. Wherefore I abhor myself, and repent in dust and ashes (Job 42:2,5,6).**

Earlier, we mentioned (Scott Huse, *The Collapse of Evolution*, and Walter Brown, *In the Beginning*) the documentation showing that the details of evolution and the specifics of Genesis 1 do not match up. For example, evolution says reptiles developed first and then birds evolved out of reptiles, but the Bible says birds came first (Genesis 1:20-23) and then reptiles (Genesis 1:24-26). If we again go back to thinking about the days of Genesis, then certain things are not logical when we hold to long periods of time. For example, God made plants on the third day (Genesis 1:12, 13), but He created insects on the sixth day. Many plants need insects to pollinate them. How could they survive more than two billion years, while waiting for insects to "evolve?"

Evolutionary theory does not have satisfactory answers for how we got here. Evolution forces us to throw out the clearly written and easily understood words of Genesis 1-11, since the two are not compatible. Do we believe the Bible or have we placed our trust in the foolish speculations of men, based on the foundation of the scientifically unprovable assumptions of so-called science (see the beginning of Chapter 2, Seven Basic Assumptions)?

Since origins are scientifically unverifiable for either evolution or creation, then we are dealing with "faith." No human was there to verify if the "Big Bang" happened. No person was there to witness God creating out of nothing.

VIRGIN BIRTH AND RESURRECTION

Many of us easily profess to believe in Jesus Christ as the virgin-born Son of the one true God and in His resurrection from the dead. We Christians believe in the virgin birth of the Lord Jesus, don't we? If we do not believe in the virgin birth of the Lord Jesus we are not going to go to Heaven because there would not be a holy and sinless Savior! Where do we learn of virgin birth? We learn of it in God's written Word.

> ...the virgin's name was Mary.... And the angel said unto her, "Fear not, Mary: for thou hast found favor with God. And, behold, Thou shalt conceive in thy womb, and bring forth a son, and shalt call his name JESUS" (Luke 1:27b, 30-31).

Does modern science tell us that we can lock up a virgin and she will emerge pregnant nine months later and ready to give birth to a baby? Absolutely not! Science says that virgin birth does not happen in humans. We Christians believe in virgin birth by faith because the Bible says so, even though this idea is totally contrary to scientific data.

We Christians also believe in the resurrection of the dead. Do any science textbooks teach that humans can be graveyard dead, and then resurrected back to life? Do you know any evolutionary scientists who would permit you to kill them tombstone dead because they knew that they could recruit their fellow Ph.D.'s three days from now to resurrect them back from the dead? Of course not! Well then, where do we get this idea of resurrection? We get it from the written Word of God, the Bible. The Bible states categorically, that without resurrection and our belief in it, we will not go to Heaven.

That if thou shalt confess with thy mouth the Lord Jesus, and shalt believe in thine heart that God hath raised him from the dead, thou shalt be saved (Romans 10:9).

...Christ died for our sins according to the scriptures; and that he was buried, and that he rose again the third day according to the scriptures; and that he was seen of Cephas, then of the twelve, after that, he was seen of about five hundred brethren at once; ... (I Corinthians 15:3b-6a).

Hell and the Lake of Fire await us if we do not believe in the virgin birth of the Lord Jesus, and in His, and ultimately our, resurrection. The primary evidence we have for resurrection and virgin birth is the Holy Bible, the written Word of God, with no supporting evidence at all from science. As a matter of fact, modern science speaks out loudly against the ideas of virgin birth and resurrection from the dead in humans. In spite of "evolutionary science," we believe what the Bible says. We believe by faith (2 Corinthians 5:7).

But then we get to the early chapters of Genesis, they are also the written Word of God, and we believe the old earth, local flood evolutionists instead of the clear teaching of the Bible. Not that we really need it, but there is plenty of experimentally verifiable science to support a global flood and a young earth (see Chapter 9). Why do we Christians accept the Biblical ideas of virgin birth and resurrection, which go against known "science," but we do not accept the biblical teaching on the age of the earth (around six thousand years, not 16 billion years) or the flood of the days of Noah (global, not local), when much true science is in support of the Bible? Perhaps we love the approval of men more than the approval of God.

For they love the praise of men more than the praise of God (John 12:43).

How can ye believe, which receive honor one of another, and seek not the honor that cometh from God only (John 5:44)?

...I will not give my glory unto another (Isaiah 48:11b).

We accept the Truth regarding virgin birth and resurrection without flinching, but we limit God to a "Trial and Error" entity not capable of "speaking the Creation into existence," but rather relying on billions of years and an evolutionary process to <u>finally</u> "get it right."

It is my contention that the main reason for rejecting a creationist view (especially in light of the statements by evolutionists which give the creationist position credence) is mankind's basic pride and rebellion. <u>Evolution allows us to be independent of God so that we do not feel any accountability to God. Evolution takes some pressure off our conscience! Our existence is explained without the need for God.</u>

The current, pervasive New Age teaching that, "we each have within ourselves the god consciousness and can achieve godhood by our own strength as we learn to look within ourselves and develop our full potential," further fans the flames of self-sufficiency, selfishness and independence from any power greater than ourselves. This New Age teaching promotes evolution and is deadly deception. It is the way of death. It leads people to reject the Lord Jesus Christ as their personal Savior. New Age evolutionary thinking also convinces people that they cannot believe the first eleven chapters of Genesis to be the literal Word of God. Truly, **"There is a way which seemeth right unto a man, but the end thereof are the ways of death"** (Prov.14:12).

FLOOD WATERS COVERED THE EARTH

Included early in Genesis is the account of Noah and the Flood. If evolution were true, then a global flood taking place about 4,500 years ago would be impossible! Evolution demands millions of years, not just a few thousand, for creatures and ecosystems to evolve. We sometimes hear this historical event referred to as the Flood of Noah. It was not Noah's flood. It was God's flood! The Flood was God's judgment on the sin that had spread to cover the earth. Genesis 6:5-14a describes God's heartbreak at the sinfulness of mankind and His recognition of Noah as the only righteous man on the face of the earth.

> **And God saw that the wickedness of man was great in the earth, and that every imagination of the thoughts of his heart was only evil continually.**
>
> **And it repented the Lord that he had made man on the earth, and it grieved him in his heart.**
>
> **And the Lord said, I will destroy man whom I have created from the face of the earth; both man, and beast, and the creeping thing, and the fowls of the air; for it repenteth me that I have made them.**
>
> **But Noah found grace in the eyes of the Lord.**
>
> **These are the generations of Noah: Noah was a just man, and perfect in his generations, and Noah walked with God.**
>
> **And Noah begat three sons, Shem, Ham and Japheth.**
>
> **The earth also was corrupt before God, and the earth was filled with violence.**
>
> **And God looked upon the earth, and, behold, it was corrupt; for all flesh had corrupted his way upon the earth.**
>
> **And God said to Noah, The end of all flesh is come before me; for the earth is filled with violence through them; and, behold, I will destroy them with the earth.**
>
> **Make thee an ark of gopher wood....**

THE DESTRUCTION
OF ALL LAND-BASED FLESH

What has God told us was His purpose in sending a global flood? Genesis 6:5 records that God saw the great wickedness and evil in mankind. Genesis 6:17 states the actual purpose of the Flood: **"... to destroy all flesh."** The types of life to be destroyed are more specifically listed in Genesis 7:21-23:

> **And all flesh died that moved upon the earth, both of fowl, and of cattle, and of beast, and of every creeping thing that creepeth upon the earth, and every man:**
>
> **All in whose nostrils was the breath of life, of all that was in the dry land, died.**
>
> **And every living substance was destroyed which was upon the face of the ground, both man, and cattle, and the creeping things, and the fowl of the heaven; and they were destroyed from the earth: and Noah only remained alive, and they that were with him in the ark.**

The purpose of this great judgment by water was to destroy all dry-land life. Dry-land life extended well beyond the Tigris and Euphrates valley! The Flood was not designed to destroy marine life, although many water creatures were destroyed by the Flood as is seen in the fossil record.

Peter tells us (2 Peter 3:5-13) that there are three heaven-and-earth systems in God's eternal plan. The first system was totally destroyed by the water of the Flood, which was the judgment of God in Noah's day. Remember it was the violence (Gen. 6:11) that moved God to judgment! (What is the content of the movies and cartoons that you and your family are watching? Have you noticed the astronomical increases in violence?)

The second heaven-and-earth system (our present system, 2 Peter 3:7) will be destroyed by fire so hot as to destroy even the foundational molecules of the earth and sky (2 Peter 3:10). The root of sin, wickedness and violence will finally be burned out of existence. So, how are you investing your resources (time, treasure, talents)? Only three things will not be burned up—God; God's Word (the Bible); and people. Are you investing eternally in God's Word and people?

The third heaven-and-earth system is called the New Heavens and New Earth (2 Peter 3:13). This eternal, righteous heaven-and-earth system is also referred to in Romans 8:21, Revelation 21:1 and perhaps Isaiah 65:17. It will last forever. Only those whose names are written in the Lamb's *Book of Life* will inherit the New Heavens and New Earth. Have you come to the sacrificial Lamb, the Creator Jesus, in faith repenting of (willfully turning away from) your sin and rebellion and believing that He alone has the power and right to save your soul? Have you committed the rest of your life to the Lord Jesus Christ and to His service? Are you justified?

Therefore being justified by faith, we have peace with God through our Lord Jesus Christ (Romans 5:1).

THE DAYS OF NOAH AND THE SECOND COMING OF JESUS

The Lord Jesus contrasted the days of Noah and the flood judgment to His Second Coming:

And as it was in the days of Noah, so shall it be also in the days of the Son of man. They did eat, they drank, they married wives, they were given in marriage, until the day that Noah entered into the ark, and the flood came, and destroyed them all (Luke 17:26, 27).

The Flood is treated in the Bible as an actual event. Noah is not some mythical character. The Lord Jesus and writers of the Bible believed and taught about a literal man named Noah and an actual global flood. Nowhere in the Bible is the Flood characterized as a local river overflow as some scholars have hypothesized. The words of Genesis 6-9 have concrete meanings in the Hebrew lexicons. These words are not phenomenonological symbols depicting a mythological event recorded by some primitive scribe whose concept of the world was limited to the banks of the Euphrates and Tigris

Rivers. This flood covered **"...all the high hills that were under the whole heaven..."** (Genesis 7:19, Emphasis added).

THE ARK OF NOAH

Would God move Noah to build an ark 437 feet long, 73 feet wide and 44 feet deep for a local river overflow? The ark was big enough to carry, on one deck, all the kinds of dry land animals needed to repopulate the earth. Scientists have estimated that Noah would have to take a maximum of about 35,000 sheep-sized animals on the ark to give us all the kinds of creatures we have today. [A comprehensive study of all aspects surrounding the ark and Flood is: *Noah's Ark: A Feasibility Study* by John Woodmorappe (Santee, CA: Institute for Creation Research), 1996.]

The ark was big enough to carry at least 125,000 sheep-sized animals. 35,000 creatures (the largest number I've seen to generate the animals we have today) could have been kept on one of the three floors in the ark. Since God brought the animals to Noah, He probably brought young animals, even baby dinosaurs. (Please do not forget that the largest dinosaur eggs yet found are no larger than a football. So the largest dinosaurs started life no bigger than a football.) Young dinosaurs would eat less and take up less space. Noah and his family could have lived on the top deck, and, I would imagine, he maintained the insects on the bottom deck. Of course, Noah may not have needed to take insects on the ark, as they may have been able to survive on floating debris.

Would you need an ark to save birds during a local river overflow? Have you ever heard of a local river overflow that lasted longer than a year? The Genesis flood did.[83] Why would God give Noah 120 years to build the ark (Genesis 6:3

---

[83] For much more information about the Flood-judgment of God read: *The Genesis Flood* by Henry Morris and John Whitcomb (Philadelphia: The Presbyterian & Reformed Pub. Co., 1961).

seems to imply that God was giving 120 years for people to repent while Noah built the ark), when it would have been much easier to move his family and flocks out of the Mesopotamian Valley? In 120 years, Noah could have moved quite a distance away from a flood if it was just a local river overflow! Dr. John Morris has an excellent video on this very subject called, *The Deluge*, filmed on location at Mt. Ararat in Turkey. It is produced by I.C.R., P.O. Box 2667 El Cajon, CA 92021, (619) 448-0900.

Could God have taken care of Noah, his family, and that ark-load of creatures for a whole year? Genesis 8:1 begins by saying, **"And God <u>remembered</u> Noah, and every living thing, and all the cattle that was with him...."** That word "remembered" (zakar) is a special word. In the text of the Hebrew language, it has the idea of intimate care and watchfulness. The concept of knowing needs and acting on that knowledge is contained in the word. It was not that Noah was stranded in the ark and God had been busy doing other things. Then God suddenly looked down and said, "Oh, my! I just remembered Noah." This word carries with it the concept of meeting needs.

Some creationists have suggested that the process of hibernation may have begun during the Flood. Perhaps many animals slept through most of the ride. Numerous animals that do not normally hibernate or estivate (hot weather sleeping) can be made to do so in certain laboratory conditions. The ability to hibernate is displayed by such animals as: bats, skunks, woodchucks, prairie dogs, badgers, bears, certain mice, humming birds, garter snakes, turtles, toads, spiders, beetles, dragonflies, grasshoppers, garden snails, etc. It is not impossible to believe that some (if not many) animals slept a good part of that year.

Many Bible "scoffers" refer to Noah and the Ark as just a myth or story and not an actual historical event. This could be, in part, because of the seeming impossibility of so few people caring for that large a number of animals. Hibernation and estivation of the animals and insects would definitely have decreased the time demands for feeding (and scooping) by the eight human ark passengers. Also, many Sunday School booklets display pictures of Noah's ark with giraffes' heads poking out of the top and other animals looking like they had to be squeezed in. Anti-creationist teachers and professors know these erroneous pictures exist in Christian literature and they use those images which have already been planted in children's minds to convince our children that there is no way Noah could get all those animals in that little ark!

No one can say exactly what went on in the huge, sealed ark, but God knew, and cared, and saw to it that the remnant of His creatures survived.

THE ALTAR, THE RAINBOW
AND THE DRUNKENNESS

Remember what happened when Noah came out of the ark? Three major things come to mind: the altar, the rainbow and the drunkenness. After his departure from the ark, the first recorded event in the life of Noah was his worship. He built an altar to the Lord and worshipped His Savior. Genesis 8:20-21:

> **And Noah builded an altar unto the Lord; and took of every clean beast, and of every clean fowl, and offered burnt offerings on the altar.**
> **And the Lord smelled a sweet savour; and the Lord said in his heart, I will not again curse the ground any more for man's sake; for the imagination of man's heart is evil from his youth; neither will I again smite any more every thing living, as I have done.**

As a result, God gave Noah the covenantal promise of the rainbow. Was the rainbow God's Covenantal sign to man that

He would never again send a local river overflow? Absolutely not! If it was a local river overflow in the known "world" of the writer's day, then the rainbow as a covenantal sign means nothing. There have been many local river overflows in the Middle East since Noah's day. And another thing—if there was no water canopy before the Flood that came down during the Flood, then there must have been rain and floods and rainbows before the Flood. In that case, the rain and the rainbow would have no special significance to Noah. The rainbow was a new experience for Noah. It meant that God would never again destroy life upon the earth with an all-encompassing flood.

The account of Noah's drunkenness may also be important in the study of creationism. There may be several reasons for the inclusion of this episode in God's eternal Word. Noah's drunkenness could very readily serve as a hint that man is no longer living in heaven-and-earth system #1 now that the Flood is over. The pre-Flood environmental and ecological system (#1) was destroyed by the Flood. The present heaven-and-earth system (#2) is different.

Reading certain selections from 2 Peter 3 presents to the reader God's eternal plan, which includes three heaven-and-earth systems: The heaven and earth of Adam and Noah (system #1); the present heaven and earth (system #2); and the New Heavens and New Earth of eternity (system #3).

> **Knowing this first, that there shall come in the last days scoffers, walking after their own lusts,**
>
> **And saying, Where is the promise of his coming? for since the fathers fell asleep, all things continue as they were from the beginning of the creation.**
>
> **For this they willingly are ignorant of, that by the word of God the heavens were of old, and the earth standing out of the water and in the water:**
>
> **Whereby the world that then was, being overflowed with water, perished:**

> But the heavens and the earth, which are now, by the same word are kept in store, reserved unto fire against the day of judgment and perdition of ungodly men.
>
> But the day of the Lord will come as a thief in the night; in the which the heavens shall pass away with a great noise, and the elements shall melt with fervent heat, the earth also and the works that are therein shall be burned up.
>
> Nevertheless we, according to his promise, look for new heavens and a new earth, wherein dwelleth righteousness (2 Peter, 3: 3-7,10,13).

It is probable that heaven-and-earth system #1 had a heavier atmosphere than our present system (#2). The increased atmospheric pressure was the result of God taking water off the surface of the earth (see Genesis 1:6-8) and putting it above atmospheric heaven or, more specifically, the expanse or firmament that the birds fly in (see Genesis 1:20). These "waters above" came down in Noah's day and may have set up the condition that quite possibly caused Noah's drunkenness.

Because the water came down as rain, the atmospheric pressure was reduced by at least one half. Alcohol fermentation rates are doubled when the pressure is cut in half. Therefore, because alcohol ferments faster and gets into your blood and brain more quickly in system #2 than it did in system #1, Noah likely was caught by surprise. He was God's righteous man. He had not forgotten to make an altar and sacrifice in worship of his Lord and Savior. Noah probably made the same amount of wine that he made before the flood. But now, in system #2, because the conditions had changed, Noah may have been caught by surprise and gotten drunk. We have no record that Noah ever got drunk before or after this incident. Perhaps one reason our Creator gives us this sad account is to hint at the difference between system #1 and system #2.

Our present heaven and earth are vastly different than the pre-Flood heaven and earth of Noah's day. That is the reason we do not have dragonflies with a wingspread of 32 inches, or chambered nautilus shells eight feet tall, or 100,000-pound dinosaurs walking the earth today. But we know they once lived. We have their fossils. And yet, people lived in system #1 and are still thriving in system #2. Only God could have designed life to work efficiently in two significantly different systems. There is no one like Him!

> **Forasmuch as there is none like unto thee, O Lord; thou art great, and thy name is great in might.**
>
> **He hath made the earth by his power, he hath established the world by his wisdom, and hath stretched out the heavens by his discretion.**
>
> **The Lord of hosts is his name. (Jeremiah 10:6,12,16)**

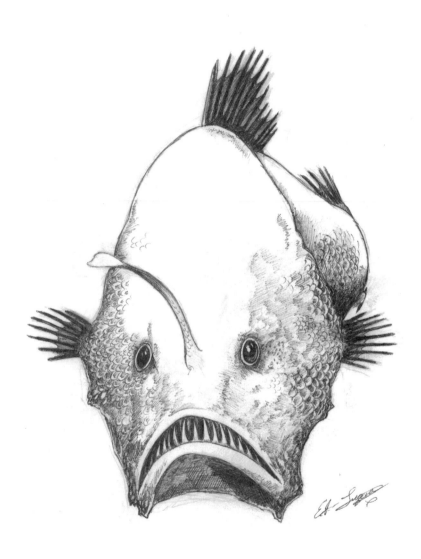

MARVEL OF GOD'S CREATION

#6

The Angler Fish

One of God's amazing creations is the deep-sea Angler fish. This fish makes its home more than a mile deep in ocean water. On her forehead the female has a "fishing rod" tipped with an "artificial worm." She dangles this "bait" over her mouth to attract her next meal. Ah, but there is a problem— her next meal cannot see the bait, since it is too dark under more than a mile of seawater. Starvation sets in while she waits for her first deep-sea fish dinner. At last, she realizes, "I must do something about this darkness problem." But, alas, it is too late. She is dead and dead fish can not evolve the adaptations needed to rectify deadly problems, even though evolution says that, given enough time, mindless, random chance processes will evolve whatever her situation (or environment) tells her is needed to survive. It may not be logical to some, but it seems to me that she would get mighty hungry waiting perhaps hundreds of years for her first meal.

The only possibility is that God created the Angler fish with all the fully-functional equipment it needed to survive at great depths. To solve the darkness problem, God created a special kind of light on the bait. This light displays highly advanced technology—it gives off no heat! A compound called Luciferin is oxidized with the help of an enzyme that scientists named Luciferase, and this reaction produces heatless light. (Research scientists have broken down Luciferase into more than 1,000 proteins, but they still do not know how the heatless light is produced. Someone someday may figure out how God made this heatless light. Need I say that they will join the ranks of the rich and famous?)

Ask an evolutionist how a deep-sea fish could evolve the ability to produce high-tech light on an artificial bait dangled over the fish's mouth? God has made His creation to display His glory and power. No one could look at the Angler fish and say it is the result of the "impersonal plus time plus chance," unless that person had already decided to refuse to believe in the God of the Bible (Romans 1). The vain speculations of macroevolution lead to foolish thinking and impossible conclusions.

Naturally, the Angler fish needs to reproduce and has a special way of doing this. In the darkness of the deep, it is difficult for the male and female to find each other. God designed the eggs of the female so that they float up through a mile of ocean to the surface. On the ocean surface, the eggs form a jellylike mass and then hatch. The young fish, male and female, grow and mature in the surface waters. At a certain point in their development, the male finds a female and bites and holds on to her abdomen. Soon the tissues of the female grow into and attach to the mouth tissues of the male, and the female drops to the bottom of the ocean carrying her parasite male with her, not to separate "'til death do they part." He found her in the light of the surface waters, so he does not have to grope around in the dark of the deep looking for a mate. How could all of this evolve when it is so ultra-specialized and unique? Why does the female not chase the male away when he bites her abdomen? What possible evolutionary mechanism enables the male's circulatory system to merge with the female's? And from what creature did this peculiar fish evolve? Evolution has no answers.

A major difference between the Angler fish and other fish is the Angler's lack of a swim bladder, which is an air sac to provide buoyancy and to prevent sinking. If it had evolved without an air bladder, it would sink and die. If it had an air bladder and had evolved the bait and light in surface waters, it would be easy prey for other predators and "survival of the fittest" would force it into extinction.

Another feature of the deep sea Angler is its special body, which is designed to prevent crushing. A pressure of over 2,000 pounds per square inch is exerted on the body of the fish at one mile deep. It survives this great pressure with no problem. On the other hand, if the first Anglers were surface fish and lost their air bladders, (through let's say, some unexplainable genetic mutation) and then sank to the bottom of the sea, they would have been crushed. Dead animals don't evolve any further.

Someone once asked what the purpose would be of the lighted bait on the Angler fish before the sin of Adam and the curse on nature? The Lord Jesus made life forms with the ability to exist in the pre- and post-Flood environments. Perhaps the lighted "bait" was used by the female to attract a male or to light up the rock surfaces so she could see her favorite plant food. None of us were there before the Fall or before the Flood and those conditions are not reproducible. But we can trust the God of the Bible and His Word. When the Lord Jesus says that things were different after the Flood, we believe Him, even if we can't seem to figure out some of the particulars.

The deep-sea Angler had to have been created with all its special equipment fully functional. God says that as we study His creation, it should cause our thoughts to focus on the Creator, give Him thanks, and honor Him as God (Rom 1).[84]

---

[84] For a wonderful look at the Angler fish and other highly specialized animals read: *The Natural Limits to Biological Change* by Lane P. Lester and Raymond G. Bohlin (Zondervan, 1984).

7

EARTH'S PRE-FLOOD WATER CANOPY AND THE DINOSAUR MYSTERY

I can remember one particular lunch period sitting in my office at Baylor College of Dentistry studying Genesis 1. Those dental students had asked me to explain to them what God meant in verses 6-8a. How often we read the Bible but don't really think about what it says. As I studied these verses, I realized that I didn't know quite what they were saying. Here is what the Bible says:

> **And God said, Let there be a firmament in the midst of the waters, and let it divide the waters from the waters.**
> **And God made the firmament, and divided the waters which were under the firmament from the waters which were above the firmament: and it was so.**
> **And God called the firmament Heaven (Gen.1:6-8a).**

It says God divided the waters and put some water above the firmament (heaven, 1:8a) and left some water under the firmament. What is this firmament? Genesis 1:20 reads:

> **And God said, Let the waters bring forth abundantly the moving creature that hath life, and fowl that may fly above the earth in the open firmament of heaven.**

The expanse or firmament of Genesis 1:7 may be the open heaven of Genesis 1:20 where the birds fly around. Now, there are several views and different interpretations of these Genesis verses, but the one that seems to make the most sense to me, and the one that I believe, is this: God separated the waters that covered the earth in the beginning and left some water on the earth and put some water up above the air where the birds fly.

EXPLAINING THE WATERS ABOVE

Before we go much farther, let us clarify the uses of the Hebrew word that is translated as expanse or firmament or heaven. There are three different heavens that are mentioned in the Bible: 1) atmospheric heaven, 2) the heaven where the stars are (stellar heaven), and 3) the third heaven where God lives (paradise). This third heaven is referred to in 2 Corinthians.

> **I knew a man in Christ above fourteen years ago…such a one caught up to the third heaven. …How that he was caught up into paradise (2 Cor. 12:2b, 4a).**

Psalm 19:1 calls our attention to both the atmospheric and stellar heavens:

> **The <u>heavens</u> declare the glory of God; and the <u>firmament</u> showeth his handiwork [Emphasis mine].**

BENEFICIAL EFFECTS OF A WATER CANOPY

What are some beneficial effects of this water canopy above atmospheric heaven? If it were a water *vapor* canopy, there would be some protection from cosmic radiation, etc. But if it were *liquid* water, it would provide maximum protection. This might help explain 900-year life spans before the Flood. Water filters out many of the harmful rays of the sun, which might speed up the aging process. For example, water blocks alpha and beta radiation penetration. Liquid water in combination with the ozone layer would block most of the ultra violet radiations from the sunlight. Combine this with filtering of the alpha and beta radiation, and earth would have been a much healthier place to live before the Flood!

Many creationists (myself included for many years) believed this water canopy could have been water vapor instead of liquid water. Water vapor initially seemed to be a more logical way to keep the water suspended above the atmosphere. Creation scientists such as Drs. Larry Vardiman, Russell Humphrys, John Baumgardner, Michael Oard, etc., have introduced problems with the water vapor canopy model and may have eliminated it as a possibility. Liquid water turns out to be a better explanation.[85]

Another advantage of the water canopy is the hyperbaric (increased pressure) effect. The weight of the water above would have increased atmospheric pressure on earth and perhaps even the oxygen content in the air. (As to increased oxygen content, scientists have found little bubbles of air in ancient amber, and the air bubbles had as much as 32% oxygen, whereas the air we breathe today in heaven and earth system #2 is about 20% oxygen.) The water canopy may have more than doubled atmospheric pressure. In this environment of heavier atmospheric pressure and higher oxygen, healing would be more efficient. Many hospitals have pressurized rooms called Hyperbaric Rooms. Into these rooms increased oxygen content is pumped under pressure and healing is miraculously speeded up. Very sick people and the severely burned are treated in this high pressure and oxygen rich environment.[86]

---

[85] Read more of their ideas at www.ICR.org and www.answersingenesis.org

[86] For more information about "Hyperbaric Therapy" see: J. C. Davis, "Hyperbaric Oxygen Therapy," *Journal of Intensive Care Medicine*, 4 (1989), 55-57. Also: *Textbook of Hyperbaric Medicine*, ed. K. K. Jain (Toronto: Hogrefe and Huber Pubs., 1990), p. 492. Also: *Hyperbaric Oxygen Therapy: A Committee Report* (UHMS PUB 30 CRHOB), ed. J. T. Mader (Bethesda: Undersea and Hyperbaric Medical Society, Inc., 1989), p. 90.

God could have made the canopy exactly the right thickness and distance from earth to enable plants to get enough light energy for their photosynthesis while blocking the harmful radiation and the excessive heat. If the water of the canopy were in the form of liquid water (perhaps under the ozone layer but above where the birds fly), it would have made heaven-and-earth system #1 (before the Flood) similar to a giant terrarium. There would have been no rain! And what does the Bible say? Genesis 2:6: **"But there went up a mist from the earth, and watered the whole face of the ground."** That is the exact effect expected if a water canopy surrounded the earth: a morning mist would form. Genesis 2:5b is more specific: **"...for the Lord God had not caused it to rain upon the earth."** No rain, therefore no rainbow! Heaven-and-earth system #1 was obviously different from our present system, system #2.

THE GREENHOUSE EFFECT

With a water canopy, a greenhouse effect would be expected due to the heat generated by the sun-warmed canopy. Is there any evidence that greenhouse warmth once surrounded our globe? Palm tree fossils have been found in Alaska and broad leaf ferns in the Arctic. How could a palm tree fossil be in Alaska? Some scientists have postulated they traveled there on the tectonic plate (earth crust) movement over millions of years. But these trees are not millions of years old! A creationist would say, "No problem, palm trees grew in Alaska in the tropical world before the Flood." These trees were buried during the Flood of Noah's day resulting in their fossilization. (It has recently been suggested that these fossils traveled to Alaska on extremely rapid tectonic plate movement instead of slow movement. This writer still thinks that they grew there.)

Scientists have found tropical forests and coal deposits in Antarctica. How did they get there if plants in past history did not grow there? Fruit trees that were quick-frozen and over ninety feet in height with green leaves have been found in the New Siberian Islands where, today, only one-inch high willows grow.[87] In these frigid zones, many trees (some fossilized and some quick-frozen) have been found in flood sediments with rings, signifying rapid, warm temperature growth. The Evolutionist asks, "How did they get here?" A Creationist might say, "They grew there before the Flood when the earth was pole to pole greenhouse warm."

A RUNAWAY GREENHOUSE EFFECT?

Of course, the idea of a water canopy will bring objections from some scientists, even creationist scientists. Would there be a problem of overheating causing a runaway green house effect? Some scientists believe that a water canopy of any kind would generate too much heat coming in to earth's atmosphere and not enough escaping, resulting in overheating and death to all life on earth. Could our Creator have designed Adam's world with a suspended water canopy (liquid, not vapor) that did not generate too much heat for life to exist?

If the water canopy was under the ozone layer [if it was above the ozone layer, this crucial protective barrier may have been destroyed when the water came down through the ozone at the Flood, and, depending on how far into space the canopy was located, there may have been a vacuum above it which would permit the water to evaporate rapidly out into space and the canopy would disappear], the liquid water in the canopy might actually be a heat and radiation shield. It would physically block off some amount of heat. The heat energy

---

[87] Charles Hapgood, "The Mystery of the Frozen Mammoths," from Bassett Digby, *The Mammoth and Mammoth Hunting Grounds in Northeast Siberia* (N.Y.: Appleton, 1926), pp. 150-151.

during the daylight part of the day could be absorbed as the water on the outer surface of the canopy evaporated. The water could then re-condense during the coolness of the night. Because of the ozone layer above the water canopy, the evaporated water would not escape into outer space.

This canopy model would actually function like a giant "heat pump" air conditioning and heating unit. In the summer, the heat in the house is picked up by the refrigerant and carried outside. The house stays cool. In the winter, the heat in the air outside the house is picked up and brought inside. The house stays warm. Water picks up heat slowly and releases heat slowly. That is why the sea breeze during the middle of a hot summer day is still cool while the inland breeze is terribly hot and vice versa during the cooler nighttime. The daylight side of the earth would be warm and the dark side cool. The differences in temperature between the two sides would balance each other out.

Even today, water in the sky (clouds) moderates the temperature here on earth. On an overcast spring day, the cloud cover can regulate the air temperature from varying by 15-20 degrees between daylight and nighttime to as little as a 2 degree difference. For example, Cleveland, Ohio, in April of 1999, had a temperature high of 70 degrees and on the same day, a low of 68 degrees as compared with 75 degrees for a high and 55 degrees for a low on clear day and night. There was only a 2-degree difference in a 24-hour period because of the cloud cover. The sun was still up there heating the top of those clouds, but under the clouds the temperature remained quite stable!

Water can absorb great amounts of heat. In the steel mills water is used to cool molten steel. One kilogram of water can cool down several kilograms of molten steel by 1,000 degrees. In the dental lab, water is used to cool and temper molten metals because it is so efficient at absorbing heat.

Our creator placed the earth and the sun in just the right relationship to each other (distance and size) and quite possibly with a water canopy above that part of the atmosphere where the birds fly, but below the ozone layer. Considering all the factors that we just discussed, we can conclude that overheating should not be a reason for us to reject the water canopy idea. This is a matter of faith. We cannot duplicate it or make it happen today, but we can believe God when he says he put water up above where birds fly. Just because current science cannot explain all the ramifications of a water canopy is no reason for us to say the canopy never existed.

THE GREAT DINOSAUR MYSTERY

Evolution has a problem called The Great Dinosaur Mystery. Where did the great dinosaurs come from? How did they grow so big? If it is "survival of the fittest," why did these powerful creatures become extinct?

A creationist would answer, "no problem." God created the giant reptiles and may have referred to one or two of them that existed in Job's day (see Job 40:15-41:34). In the pre-Flood, high efficiency atmosphere, reptiles could have grown to immense sizes, giant flying creatures could have flown more easily, and gigantism would have been much more likely.[88]

Reptiles do not have a built-in, growth-inhibiting factor like other animals and man. The dinosaurs would have continued growing as long as they lived. The older they got, the bigger they grew. God created large reptiles. Reptiles function best (cold-blooded animals) in warm temperature climates. These reptiles kept growing in an efficient high-

---

[88] Most of my comments about the effects of the water canopy came from Dr. Joseph Dillow's discussion of the effects of the vapor canopy in *The Water's Above: Earth's Pre-Flood Water Vapor Canopy* (Moody Press, 1982).

pressure atmosphere with plenty of warmth, with unlimited supplies of lush vegetation to eat, and with nothing to eat them. The Bible says,

> **And to every beast of the earth, and to every fowl of the air, and to every thing that creepeth upon the earth, wherein there is life, I have given every green herb for meat (Genesis 1:30).**

This indicates that all animals ate plants, not flesh, before the Flood. Of course, the Flood was after the Fall, and some animals may have eaten flesh because of sin or perhaps some were scavengers. But, God did not give His permission for meat eating until after the Flood (Genesis 9:1-5).

Plants themselves are a testimony to God's creative genius. They start as a seed. They take dirt, water, air and sunshine and are converted into roses, rubber and rhubarb! And these incredible factories not only do not pollute the environment, but they silently clean the air and replenish it with life-supporting oxygen. Oh, the wonders of the God of all creation!

MEAT-EATING AFTER THE FLOOD

It was only after the Flood that God gave permission to eat flesh. **"Every moving thing that liveth shall be meat for you; even as the green herb have I given you all things"** (Genesis 9:3). Nothing ate the dinosaurs before the Flood, and they had bounteous vegetation as food. They, therefore, could grow to great size during a long lifetime of hundreds of years. Even Tyrannosaurus rex ate plants, not other dinosaurs, before the Flood. The textbook pictures of this great dinosaur eating another reptile are not based on scientific method and are not supported with factual information. Tyrannosaurus most probably was a vegetarian (at least before the Flood, Genesis 1:29, 30) and used his long sharp teeth to strip leaves from plants. After the Flood, with the change in atmospheric pressure, these reptiles could never again grow so huge. The lighter atmosphere (the weighty canopy came down as rain water at the Flood), cooler average temperature, and predators would prevent long life and excessive size.

WARM BLOODED DINOSAURS?

In recent years, some evolutionists have postulated that dinosaurs were warm-blooded, not cold-blooded creatures. Warm-blooded dinosaurs have been proposed because scientists are beginning to realize that 100,000-pound cold-blooded creatures do not and could not exist in our environment. There is not enough air pressure to enable their blood to circulate properly. Somehow an important fact has escaped the notice of these evolutionists (or they are "willingly ignorant," 2 Peter 3:5). The fact is these huge reptiles would have had no problem thriving in the warm, high-pressure atmosphere of system #1. The big ones went into extinction after the Great Flood. It is not politically correct for an evolutionist to believe that the universal Flood of Noah's day actually happened. Belief in the Flood is grounds for dismissal from your job or cancellation of your grants. So, the evolutionist is left to speculate regarding "The Great Dinosaur Mystery," whereas the creationist has a valid, scientifically testable position—the environmental differences between system #1 and system #2.

Evolutionists may have theorized that warm-blooded dinosaurs would solve their dilemma, but recent research indicates that the giant reptiles were cold-blooded as are all reptiles to this day. *The Dallas Morning News*, March 21, 1994, p. 9-D, reported that three University of Pennsylvania paleontologists have published their view (in *Nature* magazine) that "...dinosaurs...were probably cold-blooded...." This is a blow to the evolutionist's dream of solving the mystery of these huge creatures! Of course, if you wait a few days some other evolutionary scientists will refute his colleagues' position. Evolutionists keep batting this "warm-blooded" or "cold-blooded" idea back and forth. *The Dallas Morning News*, July 11, 1994, p. 7-D, published a review by science reporter, Matt Crenson, of a July 1994 *Nature* magazine article. The review is partially quoted here:

> Tyrannosaurus rex had a stable body temperature, a new study shows, suggesting that the largest terrestrial carnivore was warm-blooded.
>
> Reese E. Barrick and William J. Showers of North Carolina State University in Raleigh studied Tyrannosaurus bones uncovered in the rocks of the Hell Creek Formation in eastern Montana...
>
> The remarkable consistency of the oxygen isotopes in the dinosaur's bones demonstrate that its body temperature never varied by more than about 7 degrees Fahrenheit, the North Carolina researchers wrote last week in Nature. If Montana's seasons were anywhere near as variable 70 million years ago, when Tyrannosaurus lived, as they are today, a creature with such a stable body temperature would have had to be warm-blooded.

A creationist might say that a stable body temperature in a giant cold-blooded reptile is consistent with the creationist view that the earth's temperature was uniformly warm in the tropical pre-Flood heaven and earth system number one. Creationists would expect to find "...remarkable consistency of the oxygen isotopes in the dinosaur's bones...." Apparently these evolutionistic researchers would rather pretend that cold-blooded reptiles were actually warm-blooded than to consider the pre-Flood pole-to-pole greenhouse warm condition of earth (6,000 years ago, not 70 million years ago) as presented by this creationist model.

By the way, did you know that there never was an actual dinosaur called Brontosaurus? Brontosaurus fooled the scientific community for many, many years. It turned out to be the head of one creature and the body of another. The evolutionary community was too embarrassed to admit this mistake for more than fifty years. Brontosaurus does not appear in many new textbooks. (See *The Dallas Morning News*, October 11, 1979, p. 44a.)

The giant flying reptiles such as the pterosaurs (pterodactyls and pteranodons) would be unable to fly in our present atmosphere. They needed a heavier atmosphere to get enough air to lift them with their 40 to 50-foot wingspans. Heaven-and-earth system #1 would have provided the heavier atmospheric pressure necessary for the flight of these huge creatures. Evolutionists say we don't know how these giant reptiles could have flown in our atmosphere. To a creationist, this is not a problem. Heaven-and-earth system #1, before the water canopy came down at the Flood of Noah's day, would have provided the air density needed for these huge creatures to fly.

In order to protect their jobs, the evolutionists dare not even suggest the global Flood of Noah's day as part of the solution to their problems, and yet the Flood supplies the explanation for what we "see." We even read in our older history books about many ancient cultures that taught a global flood.

GIGANTISM

Gigantism was common in the heavy pre-flood atmosphere. Fossil dragonflies with a 32-inch wingspan have been discovered and would be a frightful bug to hit your windshield! The hornless rhinoceros grew to about "...seventeen feet high and nearly thirty feet long!"[89] Giant sabre-toothed tigers, mastodons and woolly mammoths roamed the earth side-by-side with the great dinosaurs.

---

[89] Petersen, *Unlocking the Mysteries of Creation*, pp. 28,29.

MAN AND DINOSAUR COEXIST?

Man lived during the age of the dinosaurs. In cretaceous rock strata of the Paluxy River bottom near Glen Rose, Texas, human and dinosaur footprints have been found crisscrossing each other. Much has been said about these footprints because, if authentic, they prove in solid rock that man and dinosaur lived at the same time. If accepted as genuine, these footprints deal a fatal blow to evolution. They are proof that evolution is a false speculation of man! Most textbooks claim that the dinosaurs became extinct about 60 or 70 million years before man stepped onto the scene and into his footprints. Dinosaur and human footprints crisscrossing each other in the same rock strata destroys the evolutionary belief that over a period of millions of years, man evolved from his ancient reptilian ancestors!

Two Texas scientists have sectioned (cut into slices of rock) one of these human footprints. Carl Baugh and Don Patton discovered that the rock under the footprints shows pressure structures (called laminations). These pressure structures are exactly what a scientist would expect to find surrounding a human footprint! The human prints (and there are many) are not "carved" into the riverbed and neither are the dinosaur prints.[90]

In the summer of 1993, Drs. Patton and Baugh noticed eleven and one-half inch long human footprints (people have feet that big today) stepping along—left, right, left, right—inside giant three-toed dinosaur prints. Someone was walking in the soft mud of fresh dinosaur tracks! One of the tracks shows in rock the human footprint beside the dinosaur track. Apparently the person got "side-tracked" and missed one

---

[90] For more information about Glen Rose and the human footprints, contact: Dr. Don R. Patton at the Metroplex Institute of Origin Science, Inc. (MIOS), P.O. Box 550953, Dallas, TX 75355-0953 and Dr. Carl E. Baugh at the Creation Evidences Museum and Archaeological Excavations, P.O. Box 309, Glen Rose, Texas 76043 (817) 897-3200.

dinosaur print, but got back "on track" for his next step. These footprints are conclusive, hard, observable evidence that man and dinosaurs walked the earth simultaneously. For a while, *The Humanist* magazine had discredited these Paluxy River footprints to the extent that creationists withdrew their articles and films (a good film documenting the footprints is entitled *Footprints in Stone*). The summer of 1993 work by Drs. Baugh and Patton should put the shoe back on the other foot! Contact Dr. Don Patton[90] for the incredible account of how several of the footprints (but not all) were destroyed by an overly threatened evolutionist attempting to "...suppress the truth...."

Proverbs 14:12 tells us that, **"There is a way which seemeth right unto a man, but the end thereof are the ways of death."** Evolutionists travel to Glen Rose, Texas, and examine the human and dinosaur footprints side-by-side or overlapped with each other in cretaceous rock. They then concoct foolish speculations, rather than bow their knees and heads before their Creator who told us all that dinosaurs and humans existed together on the sixth day of the creation week. The Bible teaches that man and dinosaur shared the same earth at the same time (Genesis 1). This presents no difficulty since those giant creatures ate only plants before the Flood! In the early days of His creation, God prevented animals from eating each other or man, since He purposed to fill the earth with His creatures.

Another evidence to support the fact that people and dinosaurs lived at the same time in history is the cave paintings of dinosaurs. How could a "pre-historic" man or woman paint a picture of a dinosaur if he or she had never seen one? The Institute for Creation Research (www.ICR.org) and Answers in Genesis (www.answersingenesis.org) circulate excellent videos documenting the cave drawings of dinosaurs.

LONGEVITY OF LIFE

Another result of the water being above the firmament in which the birds fly would be the shielding effect from cosmic radiation. Scientists have studied how much solar radiation is filtered by water. Dr. Joseph Dillow reports their conclusions in his book, *The Waters Above: Earth's Pre-Flood Water Vapor Canopy*. In heaven-and-earth system #1, people could live to be very old. Some scientists believe that one of the primary aging factors is solar radiation. By filtering out the harmful radiation (as a water canopy would do), humans might be able to live close to 1,000 years.

The Bible reports that Adam died at 930 years of age and that Methuselah lived almost 1,000 years. After the Flood, the ages of people dropped off drastically to an average of 70 to 80 years. A lot of people think that you cannot believe the Bible when it says people lived to be 800 or 900 years old— that it must be a different kind of year or the writer did not know quite what he was talking about. Isaac Asimov, for one, said Adam did not personally live 930 years, but that his tribe lived that long.

Those old ages are 360-day years just like the Bible says (compare Genesis 7:11 and 8:3,4).[91] You can believe the Bible as it is written. Some present-day researchers who study longevity of life believe that humans could live that long again if we were sheltered from the harmful effects of the sun and the now polluted air (plus eliminate most of our mutations and disorders).

Solar shielding by the water canopy above the atmosphere where the birds fly would also affect dating techniques.

---

[91] In Genesis 7:11, the flood began on the seventeenth day of the second month and in the seventh month on the seventeenth day (five months later) as recorded in Genesis 8:4, the ark rested on Ararat. According to Genesis 8:3, these five months included 150 days — 150 days divided by five months = 30 days in a month; 30 days x 12 months = 360 days in an Old Testament year.

Negligible amounts (or none at all) of carbon 14 (C14) would have formed before the Flood.[92]

This pre-Flood water canopy can also explain one of the sources of water for the Flood. The water that God separated from the water on the surface of the earth when he said "let there be a firmament in the midst of the waters" on day two of the creation week, rained down providing some of the Flood waters (Genesis 1:6-8).

THE COLLAPSE
OF THE WATER CANOPY

And the rain was upon the earth forty days and forty nights (Genesis 7:12).

Either during or shortly after the canopy collapse (and Flood), a sudden and permanent temperature drop would occur on earth. The climate would change from being pole-to-pole greenhouse warm (heaven-and-earth system #1) to having frozen ice caps and moderate temperature (heaven-and-earth system #2). But what might have caused the water canopy to come down as rain? Several theories exist, although, of course, God does not need a naturalistic cause. He could just sovereignly command the rains of the Flood to pour down by His omnipotent power. It is possible that there was a physical mechanism that caused this liquid water canopy to disintegrate and come down as rain. For example, a cataclysmic number of simultaneous volcanic eruptions caused by the fracture of the earth's crust could be one such force. One proposed idea for the precipitation of the rain is that a meteorite slammed into the earth, shooting great clouds of dust up into the water. The dust particles would provide the

---

[92] The Institute for Creation Research is most helpful and has several different publications dealing with dating techniques. Every family should subscribe to the I.C.R. monthly newsletter, Acts and Facts, Institute for Creation Research, P.O. Box 2667, El Cajon, CA 92021 (619) 448-0900.

nuclei of condensation for the raindrops and would cause the canopy to come down. Along with this idea is the suggestion that the earth tipped 23½ degrees off dead center during this meteor's impact, resulting in frozen ice caps and the four seasons.

Another theory holds that a large number of volcanoes erupted simultaneously around the earth, and the volcanic dust provided the particles for the condensation of the vapor into rain. Perhaps all of these cataclysmic events were happening at the same time—the meteor hit the earth, fracturing the earth's crust, which in turn gave birth to multiple volcanoes.

If there was volcanic activity at the time of the Flood, then volcanic ash would be expected in deep, old ice and frozen muck. In the antarctic[93] and arctic, the oldest ice and muck is saturated with volcanic ash. The creationist position holds water. In 1893, just one volcano, Krakatau,[94] lowered the average global temperature five degrees for a year. Dust from Krakatau shot 30 miles up into the atmosphere and a series of tidal waves washed across the seas with the greatest being 120 feet high. This incredible wave pushed several miles inland on Java and Sumatra.

If the dust from one volcano (Krakatau) could lower the temperature of the earth for an entire year, what might be the chaos and cataclysm of hundreds of volcanoes erupting simultaneously? Could it be that the Bible is describing volcanic activity when it tells us that on the seventeenth day of the second month: **"...the same day were all the fountains of the great deep broken up"** (Genesis 7:11)? This was the first day of a sudden and permanent temperature drop, the effects of which are in evidence to this day.

---

[93] See Anthony Gow, "Glaciological Investigations in Antarctica," *Antarctic Journal of U.S.*, Vol. 7 No. 4 (1972), 100-101.

[94] Cheryl Simon, "Krakatau 1893: The Shock Felt 'Round the World'," *Science News*, 124 (May 1983), 138.

Science News (July 6, 1991, Vol. 140, #1, p. 7) headlines:

VOLCANO COULD COOL CLIMATE, REDUCE OZONE

The article states: "The eruption of Mt. Pinatubo could chill the Earth slightly for the next few years and hasten the destruction of the ozone layer over large portions of the world, say scientists" (p. 7). Scientific literature refers to the "Ring of Fire." Several thousand years ago, volcanoes erupted simultaneously all around the world. What caused this cataclysmic ring of fire? Could this have been the "seventeenth day of the second month?"

QUICK FROZEN ANIMALS

Evolutionary science has no answer for the existence of many quick-frozen animals found in various places around the globe. Among these frozen animals are rhinoceros, hyena, oxen, sabre-toothed tigers, hippopotamus, bison, donkeys, leopards, ibex and giant woolly mammoths. What is a quick-frozen rhinoceros doing in Siberia? Is it that he was on a little summer vacation and before he could get back to Africa, got caught in a freezing blizzard? No, there were tropical animals living in Siberia before the Flood of Noah's day! The earth was pole-to-pole greenhouse warm under the water canopy. This presents an immense problem for evolutionists. [Except for ones that claim the frozen carcasses traveled there by rapid tectonic plate movement from more tropical climates. This might transport them there, but how did they get quick-frozen in the tropics?]

What happened back then to quick-freeze tropical plants and animals in Siberia? None of these frozen "fossil" animals are transitional-form animals. All of these very ancient animals are discrete entities. They are instantly and easily classified as bison or mammoths. "Well," say evolutionists,

"It must have been a slowly creeping ice age that caught up to these animals."

The frozen animal remains do not represent a slowly creeping ice age. They were caught and permanently frozen (they are still frozen today) with such incredible speed that undigested plants remained in their mouths and in their stomach's digestive juices. Giant wooly mammoths have been discovered with undigested buttercups in their mouths and in their stomachs, which are still identifiable as to genus and species of the plant (see Dillow, footnote #88)!

What would it take to quick-freeze a happy, healthy mammoth grazing on buttercups (and several hundred other identifiable plants, which no longer grow in the frigid climate where the frozen mammoths are found)? Some scientists went to a major food-freezing company and posed this question. The answer does not fit into the known realities of heaven-and-earth system #2 (our present system).

To quick-freeze a huge, warm-blooded animal (munching on buttercups), it would take a temperature of -175°F (the coldest temperature ever recorded on earth is near -128°F) and a wind-chill factor caused by a 200-400 mph wind over a time frame of about four hours (eight hours at the outside limit). The problem is that there is nothing on earth that approaches these conditions that are necessary to freeze the animals—and yet the animals are frozen. To preserve the meat and undigested plants, drastic conditions not known on our present earth would have been necessary for the quick-freeze.

The freezing of these ancient plants and animals was not caused by a slowly creeping ice age. Many textbooks will show an artist's imaginary picture of a mammoth standing in a blizzard with a slowly creeping glacier moving up from behind. This is imagination, not reality. The mammoths were warm-temperature animals, eating warm-temperature plants in a warm-temperature climate that suddenly, in a matter of hours, became permanently frozen.

M. L. Ryder documents another interesting fact about mammoths:

> The scarcity of hair in the modern elephant is associated with a corrugation of the epidermis, and a lack of skin glands. Although the mammoth, too,...lacked glands, the increase of the hair was associated with a loss of the epidermal corrugation....
>
> Sections cut parallel to the skin surface revealed sparse, round, non-medullated hairs with no glands or erector muscles.[95]

Mammoth skin has been dissected and, to the surprise of evolutionists, it contains no sebaceous (oil) glands. Why should this be a surprise? Because cold temperature animals have a plentiful supply of oil glands to oil their hair and fur. Wolves, polar bears and seals have such oily fur that the frigid northern water rolls off and does not penetrate to the skin.

Cold temperature animals need a lot of oil to protect them from the wet cold. A mammoth could not last very long in a frigid climate without oil in its hair. It was a warm-temperature animal, eating warm-temperature plants, which was caught suddenly and frozen quickly and permanently in the distant past. Evolution provides no answer for this! A slowly creeping ice age is not a sufficient explanation for the quick-frozen animals—but a cataclysm, such as would have resulted with the collapse of the water canopy and the cataclysmic release of the fountains of the deep at the Flood of Noah's day, provides the answer and the evidence.

An animal with no oil glands in its skin cannot survive in a frigid climate. But an animal with oil glands can survive in frigid or tropical climates. Leopards have oil glands and can survive in tropical climates. Yet, their pelts have been used to

---

[95] M. L. Ryder, "Hair of the Mammoth," *Nature*, 249 (May 10, 1974), pp. 190, 191.

make fur coats that are quite warm in winter. Polar bears survive in zoos in the intense summer heat of southern states.

These mammoths (and many other animals) were frozen so quickly that their meat can still be eaten.

> In many instances, as is well known, entire carcasses of the mammoth have been found thus buried, with the hair, skin and flesh as fresh as in frozen New Zealand sheep in the hold of a steamer. And sleigh dogs as well as Yakuts themselves, have often made a hearty meal of mammoth flesh thousands of years old.[96]

This sudden and permanent temperature change from pole-to-pole greenhouse warm to the present perma-frost or permanent ice condition at and near the poles could have happened during the collapse of the water canopy at the Flood-judgment of God in the days of Noah. When the earth's crust fractured, massive volcanism would have occurred, accompanied with intense plumes of steam (See the writings of Dr. John Baumgardner at ICR and AIG). The plumes of steam would have been shooting up into the canopy and breaking through in places.

The first penetrations of the water canopy, whether by steam or volcanic activity, would have generated an effect similar to the puncturing of an air conditioner's Freon line. Instant freezing! The break-up of the canopy could have permitted heat to rapidly escape our atmosphere. This produced the frozen poles that have preserved for us animal and plant life (now extinct), which existed in heaven-and-earth system #1. Evolution has no good answer for the sudden death of the frozen animals. The Bible would lead me to believe these things happened around the time of the Flood destruction of heaven and earth system #1 (See: 2 Peter 3).

---

[96] G. Richard Lydekker, "Mammoth Ivory," *Smithsonian Reports* (1899), p. 363, as reported by Dr. Joseph Dillow, *The Waters Above*, p. 312. (See footnote #88.)

> Bless the Lord, O my soul.
> O Lord my God, thou art very great;
> Thou art clothed with honour and majesty....
> Who laid the foundations of the earth,
> That it should not be removed for ever.
> Thou coveredst it with the deep as with a garment:
> The waters stood above the mountains.
> At thy rebuke they fled;
> At the voice of thy thunder they hasted away.
> They go up by the mountains;
> They go down by the valleys unto the place which thou
>   hast founded for them.
> Thou hast set a bound that they may not pass over;
> That they turn not again to cover the earth
>   (Psalm 104:1, 5-9).

Michael Oard believes that the frozen animals and plants were entombed in the years following the Flood. The seas would have been warmer after the cracking of the earth's crust during the Flood. Evaporation from the warmer oceans would have caused huge temperature differences at the poles. This in turn would bring on mighty blizzards and the ice age.[97]

WHERE DID ALL THE WATER GO?

This naturally raises another question: where did all the canopy water go after the Flood? The answer is in Psalm 104:8,9 as quoted above. After the Flood, the water from the canopy was contained in the deep ocean valleys that sank down and the underground aquifers that remain to this day. Does that mean there was less water and more shallow seas on the surface of the earth before the Flood? Yes, that seems to be the indication.

---

[97] For more in depth information read: Michael J. Oard, *An Ice Age Caused by the Genesis Flood* (El Cajon, California: Institute for Creation Research), 1990.

OBJECTIONS TO A WATER CANOPY

Some creationists object to the idea of a water canopy surrounding planet earth before the Great Flood. They look at present phenomena and the current laws of physics and cannot imagine how a water canopy could remain suspended above our atmosphere. There are many things in God's creation that either have not been or cannot be explained by known scientific laws!

There is the 'Colossians 1:17 Principle.' This verse reads, **"And he is before all things, and by him all things consist** ("hold together," NASB)." Scientists, today, refer to the Colossians Principle to explain some phenomena in science. One such phenomenon is the positive charge of the protons not repelling each other in the tightly packed nucleus of the atom, and then the negatively charged electrons not crashing into the positively charged nucleus. You may have heard some scientists explain the same phenomenon by saying there are 'gluons' that hold the protons together and keep them from flying apart. Even if there are gluons to hold the protons together (the gluon idea is hypothetical) we are still left with the problem of electrons with their minus charge not plunging into the positively charged nucleus. So, if the liquid water canopy were in place today, we would all observe it and the scientists would find a way to explain it just like they do the proton/electron problem. They might call it the Colossians 1:17 principle or maybe they would coin a new term like 'canopy principle' or 'firmament principle' or 'raquia principle' in their attempt to help us understand what is holding the water up there (raquia is the Hebrew word for firmament or expanse).[98]

---

[98] For more information concerning objections to a water vapor canopy, look up the writings of Larry Vardiman at the www.ICR.org or www.answersingenesis.org web pages. Vardiman discusses the heat problem and potential runaway greenhouse effect of a water vapor canopy.]

There are several geological and physical explanations for the cause of the Flood based on a creationist's view. Any one view or parts of all of the views could be true—they match what we observe (science is based on observation), but my favorite is in the Bible: **"I even I do cause a Flood."** God did it! Truly He is the great **"I am that I am!"** (Exodus 3:14).

THE RAINBOW: SIGN OF THE COVENANT

The rainbow was the perfect object for God to use as the sign of His covenantal promise of no more global floods. Remember, while the canopy was still in place, the birds were flying in the expanse under this water, there were no rainbows and one must be able to see through the water (hence not perpetual clouds). The sun, moon and many stars were visible to Adam and to Noah, in view of the fact that Genesis 1:14 states that they would serve as signs. After the collapse, God signifies something new.

> **And I will establish my covenant with you; neither shall all flesh be cut off any more by the waters of a flood; neither shall there anymore be a flood to destroy the earth.**
>
> **And God said, This is the token of the covenant which I make between me and you and every living creature that is with you, for perpetual generations:**
>
> **I do set my bow in the cloud, and it shall be for a token of a covenant between me and the earth.**
>
> **And it shall come to pass, when I bring a cloud over the earth, that the bow shall be seen in the cloud:**
>
> **And I will remember my covenant, which is between me and you and every living creature of all flesh; and the waters shall no more become a flood to destroy all flesh.**
>
> **And the bow shall be in the cloud; and I will look upon it, that I may remember the everlasting covenant between God and every living creature of all flesh that is upon the earth.**
>
> **And God said unto Noah, This is the token of the covenant, which I have established between me and all flesh that is upon the earth (Genesis 9:11-17).**

Noah had never seen a rainbow in the clouds before the Flood, because it had never rained. If there was no canopy before the Flood, Noah would have experienced the same weather patterns that we have today. He would have already seen rainbows; therefore, the rainbow in the clouds would have been neither special nor new to Noah. After the Flood, when the canopy had collapsed during the forty days and nights of rain, Noah was in heaven-and-earth system #2, and was therefore experiencing our weather, rain and rainbows. He also would experience the difference between pre-flood system #1's heavy atmospheric pressure and system #2's post-flood lighter atmospheric pressure—the latter causing more rapid fermentation of alcohol and quite possibly the reason for Noah's drunkenness.

RED ALERT!

The Bible gives us a warning in Colossians 2:8:

Beware lest any man spoil you through philosophy and vain deceit, after the tradition of men, after the rudiments of the world, and not after Christ.

We must constantly be asking ourselves, "What does the Bible say?" (one of Ken Ham's favorite questions). Macro-evolution is a philosophical system and an empty deception.[99]

---

[99] When we depart from the simplicity and purity of devotion to Christ (2 Cor. 11:3), we accept empty deceptions. Many Christians have departed from Biblical Truth to believe in Darwinian evolution or in Punctuated Equilibrium (evolution did not happen too slow to see, it happened too fast to see). Stephen Jay Gould and Niles Eldredge promote "Punctuated Equilibria" as the mode of evolution [See: "Punctuated Equilibria: the Tempo and Mode of Evolution Reconsidered," *Paleobiology*, 3 (Spring 1977)]. The punctuated equilibria model (evolution is too fast to see) has been around for a long time, even though Gould seems to accept praise as the "father" of it. Punctuated equilibria is foundational to Marxist-Leninism and was seen by Marx and Lenin as essential to move people away from Biblical Truth into the vain philosophy and empty deception of Marxist-Leninism. For excellent documentation of this and Gould's roots as a Marxist, read: *The Long War Against God* by Dr. Henry Morris (Baker Book House, 1989), and *Understanding the Times* by Dr. David Noebel (Summit Ministries, Box 207, Manitou Springs, Colorado 80829, 1991).

Christians should not be taken captive by the speculative philosophy of macroevolution—there is no <u>factual</u> science (science not based on assumptions, see Dr. Kerkut's assumptions in Chapter 2) to support the molecules-to-life-to-man model of origins. Yes, evolutionists present their theories as fact. They fill our textbooks with their interpretation of the history of the universe (which leaves God out). <u>But in studying origins (where we came from), we must keep in mind that both evolution and creation are faith systems.</u>

> We must get away from thinking of evolution (molecules-to-man, ed.) as a science. It's a philosophical world-view about the past, loaded with religious implications, which historically and presently exists in a frantic attempt to explain...that we are here without a Creator/God. It results in bad science, a denial of true history, and much misery to people and nations who have adopted it.[100]

Have we allowed ourselves to be brainwashed into believing that scientific facts prove evolution of molecules-to-man to be true? No one but God was there when the universe and life appeared. Let us not be led astray from the simplicity and purity of devotion to Christ (2 Cor. 11:3)!

> **Praise ye the Lord.**
> **Praise ye the Lord from the heavens:**
> **Praise him in the heights.**
> **Praise ye him, all his angels:**
> **Praise ye him, all his hosts.**
> **Praise ye him, sun and moon:**
> **Praise him, all ye stars of light.**
> **Praise him, ye heavens of heavens,**
> **And ye waters that be above the heavens.**
> **Let them praise the name of the Lord:**
> **For he commanded, and they were created**
> **(Psalm 148:1-5).**

---

[100] John Morris, Ph.D. (Geology), *The Young Earth* (Master Books, P.O. Box 26060, Colorado Springs, CO. 80917), page 25.

Of old hast thou laid the foundation of the earth:
and
the heavens are the work of thy hands
(Psalm 102:25).

For, lo, he that formeth the mountains,
and
createth the wind,
and
declareth unto man what is his thought,
that maketh the morning darkness,
and
treadeth upon the high places of the earth,
The Lord, The God of hosts, is his name
(Amos 4:13).

The Lord hath prepared his throne in the heavens;
and
his kingdom ruleth over all
(Psalm 103:19).

MARVEL OF GOD'S CREATION

#7

The Beaver

The beaver is another uniquely designed creation. The following is copied verbatim from *Creation Ex Nihilo*, Vol. 15 No. 2, March-May 1993, pp. 38-41. Hopefully you will see the value of subscribing to this creationist magazine (contact www.AnswersInGenesis.org) as you read the words of author and scientist, Denis Dreves:

BEAVERS: AQUATIC ARCHITECTS

The dam building ability of beavers is fairly well known, but beavers possess other amazing design features which God has included in their anatomy. Beavers are air-breathing mammals which spend a great deal of time in water. For this reason they need special equipment.

First, the beaver has special valves in its ears and nose. When the beaver dives below the water these valves automatically close so that no water can enter. When the animal resurfaces, the valves reopen and it breathes again.

Perhaps their most amazing piece of equipment is their eyelids. If you have done any diving or snorkeling you will know that water and materials in it can irritate your eyes and wash out natural lubricants. Not only that, but your eyes do not see well under water. That is why snorkelers wear goggles.

Were we original to think up this idea of goggles?

Not really. God designed beavers with "built-in" goggles. Their eyelids are transparent, so they can close their eyes underwater and still see extremely well. Their transparent eyelids give protection to their eyes from waterborne irritants.

During winter, beavers must feed on the bark of trees they have cut and stored in the autumn, using their specially designed, self-sharpening front incisors (perhaps one of the beaver's better known pieces of equipment).

The beavers collect the young trees [usually two to five centimeters (one to two inches) in diameter] for food, cut them to suitable lengths and then transport them, by holding them in their teeth, to their underwater cache, forcing the branches into the mud at the bottom of the pond.

Amazing Design

Which brings us to another amazing design feature. To retrieve the stored food in the winter months when ice covers the pond, the beaver may need to chew the sticks underwater. They can do this without water entering their mouths, because they have fur mouth flaps between their front incisors and their rear molar teeth, which are set considerably further back. These two folds of skin, one on each side of the mouth, meet behind the incisors and seal off the rest of the mouth.

The beaver's large paddle-shaped tail, which has a scale-like skin covering it, is used as a rudder when it swims. This is particularly important when the animal is swimming with a branch in its mouth. The tail must compensate for any uneven drag from the branch, thus the tail is often held at an angle for accurate steering.

The rear feet of the beaver are large and webbed like a duck's feet to give the animal good swimming ability. The two inner claws of each foot have split toenails, which the beaver uses as a comb to groom itself and oil its fur.

Beavers use their smaller, unwebbed front paws to carry mud and other materials, and to dig canals which they use as a means of transporting wood and also as a means of quick escape from predators.

The fur of the beaver must be oiled to prevent water reaching the animal's skin. The oil is provided from two large oil glands. They are filled with a rich, thick, deep yellow oily liquid, which the beaver spreads on its fur for waterproofing. This, along with its two layers of fur, are so effective that water rarely reaches the skin. A layer of fat beneath the skin gives further protection against the cold.

A beaver can swim submerged for perhaps 800 meters (a half-mile) or more. Most air-breathing creatures would be adversely affected by lack of oxygen to the brain. The beaver has special equipment to compensate for this need. Large lungs and liver allow for the storage of more air and oxygenated blood. In addition, a beaver's heart beats more slowly when it dives, in order to conserve oxygen, and the blood is restricted to the animal's extremities while the vital supply to the brain remains normal.

Engineering Skills

Beavers construct dams that may be hundreds of meters long. Construction of the dam is done by cutting down trees and shrubs, dragging each piece to the dam-site, and laying them in the water parallel to the stream (end facing upstream). Almost everything the beavers can find goes into the dam—live wood, dead wood, mud, grass and rocks. When the beaver's pond floods, mounting pressure on the dam can cause it to break. To prevent this, if there is time, the beaver engineers a spillway to relieve pressure, then fixes it after the water subsides.

Beaver lodges are also the work of a master builder. They are built with sticks, and sealed from the cold with mud. The center of the roof is not sealed, which allows some ventilation. Access is only from underwater, with more than one entry in case of the need to escape. The beavers can gain direct underwater access to the cache of sticks they have stored under the water when ice covers the pond in winter and this is their only available food.

Truly the beaver is yet another example of the wonderful provision and wise planning of a caring, Creator God. Such variety of essential equipment could not have evolved over time by chance and selection. **All of the beaver's equipment must be present and fully functional in the animal from the beginning for it to survive its semi-aquatic life-style** [Emphasis added—ed.].

8

DO MUTATIONS PRODUCE
NEW LIFE FORMS?

When I began to feel the pressure of having no experimentally verifiable facts to substantiate my position as a theistic evolutionist, I turned to what I thought was my ace in the hole: Genetics. Didn't everyone know that the science of genetics had irrevocably shown evolution in progress? Without mutations (changes in the genes and chromosomes), there is no evolutionary change. The question my students asked was, "Do mutations produce new life forms or improvements in present life forms?" Naturally, I assumed they produce new forms and I thought I could prove it from the scientific literature. I was due for another rude awakening!

Many creationists[101] and evolutionists study the phenomenon of genetic mutation. Dr. Ernst Mayr of Harvard expressed the predominant view of evolutionists: "Ultimately, all variation is, of course, due to mutation."[102] Dr. Mayr instructs us that all variation (different types of plants and animals) observable in life is due to changes in the genes and

---

[101] Dr. Walter Brown wrote a paper several years ago on the evidences for creation. In his footnotes was a selection of quotes from the pro-evolutionary literature dealing with genetics. For this valuable information, please contact Dr. Walter Brown, The Center for Scientific Creation, 5612 North 20th Place, Phoenix, AZ 85016.

[102] Ernst Mayr, *Mathematical Challenges to the Neo-Darwinian Interpretation of Evolution* (Philadelphia: Wister Institute Press, 1967), p. 50.

chromosomes. These mutations occur in the make-up of DNA.

DNA: LANGUAGE OF THE CELL

DNA, the basic information system of the cell, contains the blue prints needed to manufacture 2,000 or more different proteins. Each of these proteins is manufactured in little "cell-factories" at the direction of the DNA and is essential for the maintenance of life. So, which came first? If DNA is essential in the manufacturing process of proteins, and the manufacturing process produces the proteins essential to DNA, then you can't have one without the other. This means they both must have been created fully functional and at exactly the same point in time. In other words, God must have created the information system of all cells at a point in time and fully functional. Proteins are necessary to make DNA, but DNA is needed to make proteins! DNA provides the instructions to the chemical factories inside the cell for making itself.

Scientists call DNA the "language of the cell." All scientists agree that language requires intelligence. Notice that language is information and information is non-material. Could there be an implication here that DNA, the "language of the cell," required non-material intelligence to create it? Could it be that DNA was created fully functional in all the different kinds of life by an intelligent designer God, Who ingeniously inserted thousands and thousands of pages of unbelievably complex technical information into some microscopic strands of protein called DNA? The God of the Bible, Who is infinite in His wisdom, would have no trouble here!

Evolution offers no answers to this weighty problem of the volumes of information carried by the DNA. Information requires intelligence. Evolutionary theory claims no activity of intelligence in the evolution of life forms. Yet, the God of Creation proclaims through His Holy Scriptures, "I created, created, created!"

How does a professor who is a believer in evolution on a university campus answer the following syllogism?

> Language is caused by intelligence.
> DNA is the language of the cell.
> Therefore DNA had an intelligent cause.

The professors answer with silence!

The genetic information of DNA cannot be improved upon in any normal, healthy organism. Natural selection, or "survival of the fittest," does not produce new genes; it merely selects the best-suited animal or plant life for a specific niche or environment. This is adaptation to a specific environment and not mutation. Yet, mutation is the only mechanism scientists have proposed to generate the "new" genetic information needed for evolutionary change in the molecules-to-man model. This presents an enormous problem for the evolution model, especially when we learn that mutation in a gene is a rare event.[103]

How could life have evolved into all its millions of forms if the very mechanism that causes it to evolve (mutation) is a rare event? Most scientists would agree that when mutations do occur in nature, they are either harmful to the organism or harmless (silent mutations), but there has never been an observed beneficial mutation that added new genetic information.

> The process of mutation is the only source of the raw materials of genetic variability, and hence, of evolution.... The mutants which arise are, with rare exceptions, deleterious to their carriers,

---

[103] "Although mutation is the ultimate source of all genetic variation, it is a relatively rare event..." (Francisco Ayala, "The Mechanics of Evolution," *Scientific American*, September 1978, p. 63).

at least in the environments which the species normally encounters (Theodosius Dobzhansky).[104]

Dobzhansky spent his professional life breeding and mutating fruit flies. In the end, he had somewhat strange fruit flies, but fruit flies nonetheless. Some of those flies were not even able to reproduce because they had become sterile. Dobzhansky writes that mutations are the only source of evolution, but that they are almost always harmful (which means, the mutation makes the life-form that gets the mutation in its genes, less able to survive where it lives). I might, again, add here that **mutations are harmless or neutral at best, lethal at worst, and never have been proven in undisturbed nature to be beneficial**. So, why do evolutionists continue to put so much faith in mutations as the chief mechanism for their evolutionary existence? It seems obvious that they do not want to "let a Divine foot in the door."[105]

If "survival of the fittest" is true, then the harmful mutations should contribute to extinctions, not to new and better life forms. Of course, what we observe in nature are extinctions of plants and animals rather than emerging, new life forms. There are millions of living things, from plants and animals to insects, but we hear almost weekly of more extinctions. How many newly evolved creatures have you heard about in your lifetime? With all the millions of living things in the world, surely mutations are happening, and something is or has evolved into something else somewhere. The evolutionists are frantically searching for the smallest hint that something will produce new genetic information equipping it to evolve into a new biological entity to prove their theory to be true.

---

[104] Theodosius Dobzhansky, "On Methods of Evolutionary Biology and Anthropology," *American Scientist*, Winter, December 1957, p. 385.

[105] See: Lewontin, p.34.

ARE DOGS EVOLVING?

Some of you may have heard the argument that dog-breeding experiments have proven evolution to be true. In fact, it proves just the opposite. Beginning with the Mongolian brown haired dog, you can selectively breed poodles, St. Bernards, dalmatians, golden retrievers, rat terriers, blood hounds, collies, chihuahuas or any of 250 different dog breeds. But, you obtain those dog breeds by loss of genetic information, not by gaining any new genetic information. You will never regain lost genetic material. A poodle will not revert back into another breed of dog because the genetic information has been permanently lost—unless Mr. Stud Mongrel Heinz 57 jumps over your back fence to supply some extra genetic material!

ARE GUPPIES EVOLVING?

A few years ago, the evolutionary community presented to the public one of their examples of evolution in progress. It was a guppy family that had been separated from their old friends for several years. When the guppies were reunited, they would not mate. Evolutionists consider a life-form to be a new species when it will no longer mate with its old friends. Maybe the guppy didn't smell good when it came back from its temporary environment. Or maybe its old friends didn't recognize it, or maybe the researchers didn't wait long enough to see if the guppy would be accepted again. The fact is that both populations of guppies were still unmistakably identifiable to scientists and laymen as guppies. <u>Where is the evidence for the evolution of one creature into another when, after eleven years of breeding guppies, they are still guppies</u>?

Even if these fishes refuse to breed with each other and are therefore categorized as a new species of guppy, does this prove evolution of one kind into another kind of creature? People have devised their definitions of and limits to species, but God refers to "kinds" in the Genesis account. Biblically, there are certain boundaries that no living form can cross. A specific "kind" of creature will never evolve into another "kind" of creature. Guppies are fish. Within the fish-kind there is a lot of room for change, even "evolutionary" change, but fish will forever be fish—big ones, little ones, fresh water and salt water, but still fish.

Is there intellectual integrity and honesty when scientists tell us in school and college that the chief mechanism in our ever upward and onward evolutionary process is mutation in the genes when they say in the scientific literature that mutations are harmful or deadly or neutral? "Mutations are more than just sudden changes in heredity; they also affect viability, and, to the best of our knowledge, invariably affect it adversely" (Evolutionist C.P. Martin).[106,107,108]

So, we learn that mutations in a healthy life-form invariably cause harmful changes or death (lethal) to the organism. How does evolution from molecules-to-man occur if the very process that supposedly causes it to happen, in truth, harms or kills the organism? To put this another way, why did the evolutionary scientists evacuate the area when the Three Mile Island nuclear reactor in Pennsylvania and the one in Russia at Chernobyl leaked radiation? Why didn't these scientists move their families into the area to be irradiated so mutations might develop and they could evolve into the next higher life form? The scientists knew that their

---

[106] C. P. Martin, "A Non-Geneticist Looks at Evolution," *American Scientist*, January 1953, p. 162.

[107] "If we say that it is only by chance that they (mutations) are useful, we are still speaking too leniently. In general, they are useless, detrimental, or lethal" [W. R. Thompson, *Introduction to the Origin of Species*, by Charles Darwin (New York: E. P. Dutton, 1956), p. 10].

[108] "Lethal mutations outnumber visibles (Albinism, Dwarfism, Hemophilism) by about 20 to 1. Mutations that have harmful effects are even more frequent than lethal ones" [A. M. Winchester, *Genetics*, 5th ed. (Boston: Houghton Mufflin Co., 1977), p. 356].

offspring would inherit unhealthy characteristics from the radiation. They got away from the mutation-causing radiation as fast as they could!

Professor of Genetics at the University of Wisconsin, James Crow writes:

> ...mutants would usually be detrimental. For a mutation is a random change of a highly organized reasonably smoothly functioning living body. A random change in the highly integrated system of chemical processes which constitute life is almost certain to impair it—just as a random interchange of connections in a television set is not likely to improve the picture.[109]

Dr. Crow's analogy is accurate. All of us know that stirring up and haphazardly reattaching wires in the back of a T.V. set will not improve the picture. In the same way, random changes in the genes do not improve our ability to live and function. As a matter of fact, no scientist has yet observed a random mutation produce a new hormone, enzyme, or simple organ.[110] Nevertheless, they teach us and our children the lie that we are here because our primeval ancestors had mutations occur in their genes that caused them to evolve higher and higher until, here we are. Magic! Listen to the words of the famous evolutionist from the University of Pennsylvania, Dr. Loren Eiseley:

---

[109] James Crow, "Genetic Effects of Radiation," *Bulletin of Atomic Sciences*, 14 (1958), p. 19-20.

[110] "Do we, therefore, ever see mutations going about the business of producing new structures for selection to work on? No nascent organ has ever been observed emerging, though their origin in pre-functional form is basic to evolutionary theory. Some should be visible today, occurring in organisms at various stages up to integration of a functional new system, but we don't see them: there is no sign at all of this kind of radical novelty. Neither observation or controlled experiment has shown natural selection manipulating mutations so as to produce a new gene, hormone, enzyme system or organ" [Michael Pitman, *Adam and Evolution* (London: Rider Press, 1981), pp. 67,68].

With the failure of these many efforts [to prove evolution to be true], science was left in the somewhat embarrassing position of having to <u>postulate theories of living origins which it could not demonstrate. After having chided the theologian for his reliance on myth and miracle, science found itself in the unenviable position of having to create a mythology of its own</u>: namely, the assumption that what, after long effort could not be proved to take place today had in truth, taken place in the primeval past [Emphasis added].[111]

PLANT EVOLUTION

One of the world's leading experts on plant evolution and fossil plants, Dr. E. J. H. Corner of Cambridge University dogmatically states:

> The theory of evolution is not merely the theory of the origin of species, but the only explanation of the fact that organisms can be classified into this hierarchy of natural affinity. Much evidence can be adduced in favour of the theory of evolution— from biology, bio-geography and paleontology, but I still think that, to the unprejudiced, **the fossil record of plants is in favour of special creation** [Emphasis added].[112]

According to expert Corner, there is no evidence for the evolution of plants. In fact, when plants are studied closely they appear to be a special creation!

A good example of a "very special creation" in the plant kingdom is the Ophrys stylidium orchid. One day I typed "flower" into my Internet search engine and that led me to the Ophrys orchids. You will most probably never have read about the stylidium orchid in your public school or university textbooks because it is impossible to describe in evolutionary

---

[111] Dr. Loren Eiseley, *The Immense Journey* (New York: Random House, 1957), p. 199.

[112] E. J. H. Corner, *'Evolution' in Contemporary Botanical Thought*, eds. Anna M. Macleod and L. S. Cobley, Oliver and Boyd, for the Botanical Society of Edinburg, 1961, p. 97. As quoted (partially) from *The Quote Book*, p. 11.

terms! This amazing little flower is designed to bring glory to its Creator, the Lord Jesus Christ.

The orchid has its petals and on the end of one of the stamens (little things that stick up in the middle of a flower) is a configuration that looks like a certain species of female wasp. How does evolution explain a flower that mimics a particular insect? The aroma that the orchid puts out is the same aroma that the female wasp puts out when she is looking for Mr. Wasp. So Mr. Wasp is flying around looking for Mrs. Wasp and he smells the aroma. He looks down and sees Mrs. Wasp, but it is the flower mimicking the female wasp. Mr. Wasp swoops down and lands on the flower. Well, does he get a big surprise! The part of the flower that looks and smells like Mrs. Wasp is on a hinge-action, spring-loaded joint. When the male lands on this part of the flower, the spring-loaded joint flips him down into the flower and pollen sacs attach to his head.

As the astonished male wasp climbs out of the flower, he must be thinking, "I think I'll find a different Mrs. Wasp." He is fooled again and is "popped" into another orchid. This time the pollen sacs on his head are exchanged for some new ones and he just pollinated the orchid. For two weeks, the male goes from flower, "pop," to flower, "pop," to flower.

Two weeks after the males mature, the females mature. Once the real Mrs. Wasp comes on the scene, the male will never again go back to the orchid. Here is another problem for the evolutionist: The timing must be perfect or the orchid will not be pollinated and will go extinct in one generation. There is a two-week window when the flower is mature and ready to pollinate, which must be the same two-week window when the male wasp is mature and is looking for the female wasp, but it must be the same two weeks that she is not yet on the scene!

The even more amazing fact is that there are many varieties of these orchids and each one mimics a different wasp or bee or fly! It is such a shame that there are so many truly wonderful things that our dear Lord has made for us to enjoy and <u>for us to study and to give him glory and praise,</u> and we have been taught nothing about them. As of 2002, they still are not in our children's textbooks.

The field of botany (plants) does not prove evolution. Yet, evolutionists like Dr. Corner still believe in an evolutionary mythological system. He is trusting his compatriots in "biology, bio-geography and paleontology" to prove evolution to be true. In Corner's field (plants), special creation appears to be the best option. AND, PUTTING ALL THE EVIDENCE TOGETHER, SPECIAL CREATION IS THE BEST OPTION!

If there is no evidence for the evolution of people or plants, then is there any evidence for the evolution of fish?

EVOLUTION OF FISH

The geological record has so far provided no evidence as to the origin of the fishes,...[J.R. Norman (British Museum of Natural History)].[113]

According to these experts, there is no evidence for the evolution of plants, and no evidence for the evolution of fish. What about amphibians?

EVOLUTION OF AMPHIBIANS

...none of the known fishes is thought to be directly ancestral to the earliest land vertebrates. Most of them lived after the first amphibians appeared, and those that came before show no evidence of developing the stout limbs and ribs that characterized the primitive tetrapods.... Since the fossil material provides no

---

[113] J. R. Norman, "Classification and Pedigrees: Fossils," in *A History of Fishes*, 3rd ed., ed. Dr. P. H. Greenwood, British Museum of Natural History, London, 1975, p. 343. As quoted (partially) from *The Quote Book*, p. 11.

evidence of other aspects of the transformation from fish to tetrapod, <u>paleontologists have had to speculate how legs and aerial breathing evolved</u> [Barbara J. Stahl (Emphasis added)].[114]

No evidence for the evolution of plants and no evidence for fish. What's more, the only evidence for amphibians is the "speculations" of the fossil experts. Speculation is just a big word for "guess." A guess is not proof that legs and aerial breathing evolved! The evidence, then, for evolution of creatures, as they supposedly developed the ability to crawl out of water and live as land animals, is in the imagination of the evolutionist. There are no fossils and no facts to support belief in the evolution of amphibians from fish. How about birds?

EVOLUTION OF BIRDS

The [evolutionary] origin of birds is largely a matter of deduction. There is no fossil evidence of the stages through which the remarkable change from reptile to bird was achieved (Evolutionist, W.E. Swinton).[115]

The evolution of birds is a "matter of deduction." "Deduction" in this case is a polite synonym for imagination. The evolutionists are back to guessing again. There is not a single, undisputed fossil that shows the evolutionary transitions of cold-blooded reptiles into warm-blooded birds.

THE PACIFIC GOLDEN PLOVER

The Pacific Golden Plover is a good example of a bird that cannot be described in evolutionary terms. Alaska is its summer nesting grounds and Hawaii its winter home. Golden

---

[114] Barbara J. Stahl, *Vertebrate History: Problems in Evolution* (New York: McGraw-Hill, 1974), pp. 148,195. As quoted in *The Quote Book*, p. 11.

[115] W. E. Swinton, "The Origin of Birds," Chapter 1 in *Biology and Comparative Physiology of Birds*, A. J. Marshall, ed., Vol. I (New York: Academic Press, 1960), p. 1. As quoted in *The Quote Book*, p. 11.

plover hens raise their young each summer in Alaska. As soon as the young can fend for themselves, the adults take off for Hawaii, leaving the young behind. The young must gain strength and weight to get ready for their long flight to winter with their parents.

The average weight of the golden plover before it leaves Alaska to fly to Hawaii is 200 grams. It is a small bird about the size of a pigeon. It is also a bird that does not swim! Researchers have concluded that 70 grams of its 200 grams is burnable energy. The rate at which the bird burns fuel when flying is about one gram per hour. This means right at 70 hours of flight is possible. Now we have a potentially disastrous situation. The flight to Hawaii takes 88 hours of continuous, non-stop flight! The little bird must fly for three days and four nights without food or rest or stopping at all. Impossible! How does it do this?

The birds fly in a formation that breaks the wind, taking less energy to fly. New leaders are constantly rotating in and out. Formation flight saves energy and when the birds arrive in Hawaii, they have as much as 6 grams of fuel left over. God must have built the reserve fuel supply into the plover in case of a strong head wind along the way.

Scientists are not certain how the plovers navigate from Alaska to Hawaii and back, since there is no land under their flight path. Utilization of earth's magnetic field seems to be the best solution at this point. Some have suggested that they use the sun and stars. And how do the young birds find their way to Hawaii without an experienced adult guide, weeks after their parents have already flown back to Hawaii? A one-degree mistake in navigation over the more than 4,000 kilometer flight and the birds miss Hawaii completely! But they never miss! <u>The God of the Bible is the guiding force behind the incredible endurance and navigational abilities of</u>

the little golden plover. Nothing is too difficult or impossible for our Creator!

> **Ah Lord God! behold, thou hast made the heaven and the earth by thy great power and stretched out arm, and there is nothing too hard for thee (Jeremiah 32:17).**
> **Behold, I am the Lord, the God of all flesh: is there any thing too hard for me (Jeremiah 32:27)?**

A major problem for evolution is the migration of the golden plover over ocean water with no place to rest between Alaska and Hawaii. Evolutionists usually teach that migratory animals learn their migratory routes over time and with experience. Let us imagine a newly evolved bird that will evolve into a migratory bird. Our warm-blooded bird arrives in Texas after a lengthy, mindless, purposeless, random chance, accidental evolution from a flightless, cold-blooded reptile. [How does a cold-blooded reptile give birth to a warm-blooded bird? This is a major leap of faith for an evolutionist!]

Our evolving bird discovers that Texas gets a bit too cold in winter, so it flies down to Mexico for the winter. Each year or so, it flies further north for the summer and further south for the winter. Finally, it finds just the right climate for summer and winter and migrates between these two places from then on. I think the God of the Bible made the little Pacific golden plover to totally discredit this kind of evolutionary teaching! It had to make its full migratory flight the very first time (and every time after that) or it would drop into the ocean and drown.

According to the evolutionary experts cited above, evolution is grossly lacking in hard evidence! Although we are told that mutations are good because they generate new life and produce evolution, we do not see this "good" happening in reality. Genetic mutations cannot be the driving force behind evolution. Nor do the evolutionists provide evidence to prove the evolution of any creature.

TIME GENERATES MIRACLES

But what if earth history was counted in billions of years? The old argument always comes along at this point that anything can happen in a mindless, purposeless, totally random chance, accidental system, if it is given enough time. The miracle of life can come from informationless dead chemicals if given enough time. We will discuss the "billions of years" argument in Chapter 9.

FOR YOUR INFORMATION!

A short discussion of "information" may be helpful at this point. Dr. Werner Gitt is a specialist in information transmission and technology. In his informative book, *In the Beginning was Information*, he records several impossibility theorems dealing with information.

It is impossible to set up, store, or transmit information without using a code.

It is impossible to have a code apart from a free and deliberate convention.

It is impossible that information can exist without having had a mental source.

It is impossible for information to exist without having been established voluntarily by a free will.

It is impossible for information to exist without all five hierarchical levels: statistics, syntax, semantics, pragmatics, and apobetics.

It is impossible that information can originate in statistical processes.[116]

Dr. Gitt continues by saying:

---

[116] See: Werner Gitt, *In the Beginning was Information* (Bielefeld, Germany: Christliche Literatur-Verbreitung e. V.), 1997, p.80.

Information is nonmaterial, but it requires material media for storage and transmission.

Information is not life, but the information in cells is essential for all living beings. Information is a necessary prerequisite for life.

Life is nonmaterial, and it is not information, but both entities, matter and information, are essential for life.[117]

According to Dr. Gitt, information is not life, but is necessary for life (as we all know). Since information needs a code, and a code requires a mental source, mindless evolution of new genetic information is technically impossible!

Before leaving Chapter 8, let us not forget that changes in the information content of the genes (random mutations) do not improve present life-forms. Nor is there any solid factual evidence that mindless, random genetic changes generate new information for plants or animals. The evacuation of Three Mile Island and Chernobyl to escape radiation leaks spoke volumes! (If, indeed, mutations are helpful and information can be added to the genes, then we should gladly and willingly expose ourselves to radiation-caused gene changes to "improve" our evolutionary opportunities and evolve into the next higher life form!)

---

[117] Ibid., p.81.

When I consider thy heavens, the work of thy fingers, the moon and the stars, which thou hast ordained;

What is man, that thou art mindful of him? and the son of man, that thou visitest him?

For thou hast made him a little lower than the angels, and hast crowned him with glory and honour.

Thou madest him to have dominion over the works of thy hands; thou hast put all things under his feet:

All sheep and oxen, yea, and the beasts of the field;

The fowl of the air, and the fish of the sea, and whatsoever passeth through the paths of the seas.

O Lord our Lord, how excellent is thy name in all the earth (Psalm 8:3-9)!

MARVEL OF GOD'S CREATION

#8

The Chicken Egg

A fertilized chicken egg is a very special creation. Before even thinking about a chick developing in an egg, it is interesting to ponder how the chicken manages to get a shell around that slippery, raw, fertilized egg. It is a rare sight on the farm to see raw egg smeared on the outside of the shell. Have you ever attempted to put an egg back into its shell after it rolled off the counter?

The shell itself is highly specialized. Each chicken egg shell has about 10,000 tiny holes or pores. How does that chicken form a shell around a soft, messy egg and design the shell to have porosity? Put a raw egg in warm water and soon you will see tiny bubbles floating up. These bubbles are escaping through the pores in the shell. The developing chick needs these pores to breathe. Evolution basically says that when a need arises in an organism, mindless, random chance processes provide exactly, precisely and specifically what the organism needs to alter and improve it so that it will survive. How does a chicken know it needs to make a shell with porosity, and how would mindless evolution manufacture such a shell? The chick does not know it needs the holes in the shell to breathe until it dies for lack of air. Of course, dead chicks cannot evolve.

Within the first few days after the egg is laid, blood vessels begin to grow out of the developing chick. Two of these attach to the membrane under the eggshell and two attach to the yolk. By the fifth day, the tiny heart is pumping blood through the vessels. What makes those blood vessels grow out of the chick, and how do they know where to go and to what to attach? The chick feeds from the yolk with the yolk vessels and breathes through the membrane vessels. If any of these vessels do not grow out of the chick or attach to the correct place, the chick will die.

The chick gives off carbon dioxide and water vapor as it metabolizes the yolk. If it does not get rid of the carbon dioxide and water vapor, it will die of gaseous poisoning or drown in its own wastewater. These waste products are picked up by the blood vessels and leave through the pores in the eggshell. What evolutionary chance happening provided for all of these crucial advancements?

By the nineteenth day, the chick is too big to get enough oxygen through the pores in the shell. It must do something or die. How does it know what to do next? By this time, a small tooth called the "egg-tooth" has grown onto its beak. It uses this little tooth to peck a hole into the air sack at the flat end of the egg. When you peel a hard-boiled egg you notice the thin membrane under the shell and the flattened end of the egg. This flattened end, which looks like the hen did not quite fill up her egg shell, is the air sack. The air sack provides only six hours of air for the chick to breathe. Instead of relaxing and breathing deeply, with this new-found supply of air, the chick keeps pecking until it breaks a small hole through the shell to gain access to outside air in adequate amounts.

On the twenty-first day, the chick breaks out of the shell. If one step in the development of the chick is missing or out of order, the chick dies.[118] Timing is absolutely crucial!

---

[118] Bob Devine, *God In Creation* (Chicago: Moody Press, 1982), pp. 9-13. This booklet discusses ten of God's creations and shows how they could not have evolved. There are a series of these booklets.

Each step in the development of the chick defies evolutionary logic. The process must be orchestrated by God, our Creator. The impersonal plus time plus chance is not an adequate explanation for the wondrous complexities of life as we observe it. There had to be a Designer and His name is the Lord Jesus Christ (John 1; Colossians 1; Hebrews 1).

9

EARTH: YOUNG OR OLD? GIVE ME FACTS, NOT ASSUMPTIONS

When faced with a lack of evidence to support their faith system, the evolution of molecules to man, the evolutionist will always fall back on the argument of "time." "Give us enough time," they say, "and evolution will occur." And so the evolutionists publish dates of billions of years for the age of the universe. These "billions and billions of years" are emphasized from our childhood days. As little children, we hear famous people and "credentialed" science writers in white lab coats over and over again and again refer to these long ages of time. News broadcasters and public television nature programs refer to billions of years as a matter of fact. **Repetition is essential to brainwashing; brainwashing is essential to belief in dead-chemicals-to-one-living-cell-to-man evolution, since there is no factual science (science not based on assumptions) to back it up.** Macroevolution cannot be proven to be true since no one was there but the Creator to witness The Beginning. Hence, both evolution and creation are faith systems.

Most creationists would say that the universe is somewhere between 6,000 to 10,000 years old. (The Bible shows the universe to be about 6,000 years old via the biblical genealogical tables). A young universe is not a problem for creationists because our God, the Creator-God of the Bible, is also the Creator of time. He does not need long ages of time. He can and did create people, plants and animals fully mature, but only seconds old.

What if someone was able to take a piece of one of Adam's bones on the sixth day of the creation week (the day Adam was created) and to send it to a C14 dating lab? How old would the lab claim Adam's bone to be? Probably thousands of years old, even though it was only one day old, because they would not find any C14 in the bone. Of course, on the sixth day of the creation week, Adam would not have had time to eat plants containing C14 and the C14 then would not have been transported to his bones. So, a very old, but very false date would be obtained for Adam's age. (With the water canopy in place before the Flood, almost no C14 would have been formed in that atmosphere anyway. So, on the day of Adam's death, 930 years later, the C14 lab would most probably still publish Adam's bones to be thousands of years old since they would, even at the end of his life, again find little or no C14.)

This brings up another problem with C14. Dr. Willard Libby, the discoverer and inventor of the C14 method for dating organic material, noticed a problem. If the earth were older than 30,000 years, C14 and C12 would be in a steady state of equilibrium with each other. The problem is that they are not yet in that steady state of equilibrium! As a matter of fact, there is more than a 25% discrepancy between C14 and C12. This can mean only one thing. THE EARTH AND ITS ATMOSPHERE ARE LESS THAN 30,000 YEARS OLD!

Using C14 to date anything older than about 4,500 years (The Flood of Noah's day when the protective water canopy collapsed was about 4,500 years ago) may very well produce a totally false age determination. There are published reports of detectable amounts of C14 in coal deposits. This coal must then be only a few thousand years old and not 10 to 20 million years old! [See ICR and AIG web pages.]

Since accurately obtaining very old ages utilizing C14 is biblically impossible, then what can we say about the dating techniques commonly used to date rocks with ages determined to be millions and even billions of years old?

The evolutionists make major assumptions during the course of determining a date of several million or billion years for the age of a piece of rock. If any of their assumptions are invalid, then it is impossible to use that technique to find a correct age for the rock.

Here is how these dating techniques work: Let us say we find a rock and then want to determine how old it is. We decide to analyze the rock by looking for certain elements or compounds which break down over time into certain other elements or compounds. We might look for a special isotope of uranium and the element it eventually breaks down (decays) into, which is lead. In our rock specimen, we find some of this special uranium and some of the lead it decays into (the "daughter" element).

The lead is called the daughter element because it comes from the breakdown of its mother element, uranium. We can measure how much lead is in the rock, and because we think we know how fast (or slowly) the uranium would decay into the lead, the amount of lead in the rock should then tell us how old the rock is. In other words, the amount of lead present in the rock would have resulted from a certain amount of uranium decaying over a certain number of years into lead. For all of this to yield a specific time frame in millions or billions of years, certain assumptions are made.

ASSUMPTION ONE: NO DAUGHTER COMPONENT

First, it is assumed by the rock-dating expert that the system must have initially contained none of its daughter component. In order to accurately calculate the age of a rock specimen, there can be no lead (daughter) in the original rock. It takes 4.5 billion years for half the amount of uranium to decay into a certain amount of lead. We analyze a rock and discover it has that certain amount of lead in it. The article we publish would state, with full conviction, "This rock was 4.5 billion years old as scientifically dated using high-tech procedures by Dr. Credentials who has a double Ph.D. in rock dating." Who will doubt how old the rock is? Almost no one. But hold on for a minute. Suppose God created that rock with some of the lead (daughter) already in it. How can the expert differentiate between the lead that God put there originally and the lead that came from uranium decay?

Science tells us there is absolutely no difference in the physical and chemical properties between the lead in the specimen that has been lead since the beginning and the lead that came through the decay process. So, no one can know how much lead was there to begin with. Consequently, for laboratory "accuracy" the evolutionist must arbitrarily decide, "There was no lead (daughter element) there to begin with; I can't prove it, but I will assume (pretend) this to be true."

It is mathematically impossible to have two variables in one equation and to be able to solve the equation. One variable in every rock dating equation that is unknown is the initial amount of the daughter element and the second unknown variable is the age of the specimen. Yet claims are constantly made that one can determine the age of the rock in spite of the two unknowns.

An example of this could be a burning candle. If you walk into a room and find a candle burning, you can measure the rate at which it is burning. Assuming that it has been burning at that constant rate the entire time, can you determine 1) how tall that candle was when it was lit and 2) how long it has been burning? The answer to this is an emphatic no! There are two unknowns in a single equation.

Every time you are told that a rock is several million or billion or even tens of thousands of years old, the scientist doing the dating has assumed no daughter element initially existed. This means he guesses every time. **Do we take scientists' guesses as valid fact and then proceed to the belief that the Bible must be wrong when it talks of 24-hour creation days about 6,000 years ago? Surely not!**

ASSUMPTION TWO: NO CONTAMINATION

The second assumption of the scientist dating the rock is that his specimen of rock had never been contaminated. Nothing could have come into or out of the rock that could alter the dating analysis to give an erroneous date. This would demand an "Isolated System" for the rock's environment. As Dr. Henry Morris says in *Scientific Creationism*,[119] there is no such thing in nature as an isolated system. The closed system is an ideal concept convenient for analysis, but non-existent in the real world. Morris mentions that the idea of a system remaining isolated for millions of years becomes an absurdity.

One reaction that even more seriously alters the dating data is the radioactive radon gas that is one of the intermediates of the thirteen-step decay process of uranium becoming lead. Radon gas is an inert element that does not chemically react with any other element and therefore stays in a gaseous state. A radioactive element that is a gas and has a half-life of several years would have bubbled away from the rock specimen that is being analyzed. Extremely high temperatures and varying pressures, which are predicted in the old earth model, would also affect the bubbling away to various degrees. The result of this gain and/or loss of daughter

---

[119] Dr. Henry Morris, *Scientific Creationism* (San Diego: Creation-Life Pubs., 1974), Chapter VI.

and intermediate elements (such as radon gas bubbling away) would seriously affect the ability to accurately date the rock.

Some evolutionists claim that every molecule in the universe has been in at least four different substances since the Big Bang. But evolutionists cannot have both; they cannot have molecules jumping around from one substance to another and molecules steadfast and immovable, as they would have to be in the isolated system in order to make their dating techniques work.

Therefore, the second assumption needed to affix old dates to rocks is not valid. Rocks do get contaminated as things seep into them, and rocks change their constituents as things leech out and bubble out of them. An isolated system sounds good and must be assumed to have accuracy in dating rocks, but it does not occur in nature.

ASSUMPTION THREE: CONSTANT DECAY RATE

The third assumption listed by Dr. Henry Morris (*Scientific Creationism*, p. 138) is that, "The process rate must have always been the same." Remember our candle analogy from assumption #1? What if there was an additional complication? What if the candle was not burning at a constant rate? What if a breeze had blown across it for a few minutes right after it was first lit which made it burn faster? That would make the equation contain three unknown variables. If it is impossible to solve an equation with two unknowns, it will not help a whole lot to add a third unknown!

If the process rate (the speed at which the mother element breaks down into the daughter element) has ever changed since the rock was formed, then the change of rate of decay would have to be known for the age calculation to be accurate. Scientists now know that process rates can be altered by various factors. Decay rates can be speeded up or slowed down in certain substances when subjected to various types of radiation, heat and pressure. As Dr. Morris states, every process in nature operates at a rate that is influenced by a number of different factors (p. 139).

Let's also look at this the other way around: if there were no changes in the decay rate, then the third of the three dating assumptions listed above might be correct even though the other two would of themselves destroy the accuracy of the dating technique.

"EDUCATED GUESSES" FOR DATING ROCKS?

Dr. Morris says that educated guesses are made to determine apparent ages. But the apparent age may be completely unrelated to the true age of the rock. Guesses must be made when rocks are dated at millions of years if it has been only 6,000 years since every rock in the universe was created! If 6,000 years old is the oldest possible age of any rock in the universe, then how do the rock-dating experts arrive at millions or billions of years? Dr. Richard Mauger, Ph.D. in Geology, puts it this way:

> In general, dates in the "correct ball park" are assumed to be correct and are published, but those in disagreement with other data are seldom published nor are the discrepancies fully explained.[120]

"Assumptions determine conclusions," so if the assumptions are not valid, then the conclusions (as in the age of rocks) will be wrong. If the primary assumption is that the universe is billions of years old, then the dating techniques will be calibrated to render vast old ages when rocks are dated. The "correct ball park" will be billions of years, even when the rocks cannot be older than 6,000 years.

---

[120] Mauger, Richard Ph.D., "K-Ar Ages of Biotites from Tuffs in Eocene Rocks of the Green River, Washakie and Uinta Basins of Utah, Wyoming and Colorado," *Contributions to Geology*, vol. 15(1), 1977, p. 37, University of Wyoming.

THE THREE ASSUMPTIONS

These three assumptions: (1) no original daughter element, (2) a closed system, and (3) the same decay rate throughout all time—are always involved when a scientist dates a rock. <u>None of these assumptions are valid, and none are able to be subjected to the scientific method of observation and reproducible experimentation</u>. There is no way to accurately date anything beyond several thousand years. That means the earth could be quite young and no scientist can absolutely prove otherwise!

> ...there is certainly no real proof that the vast evolutionary time scale is valid at all.
>
> That being true, there is no compelling reason why we should not seriously consider once again the possibilities in the relatively short time scale of the creation model.
>
> As a matter of fact, the creation model does not, in its basic form, *require* a short time scale. It merely assumes a period of special creation sometime in the past, without necessarily stating when that was. On the other hand, the evolution model does *require* a *long* time scale. The creation model is thus free to consider the evidence on its own merits, whereas the evolution model is forced to reject all evidence that favors a short time scale.
>
> Although the creation model is not necessarily linked to a short time scale, as the evolution model is to a long scale, it is true that it does fit more naturally in a short chronology. Assuming the Creator had a purpose in His creation, and that purpose centered primarily in man, it does seem more appropriate that He would not waste aeons of time in essentially meaningless caretaking of an incomplete stage or stages of His intended creative work.[121]

The truth is that we have been taught a lie from our earliest school days.[122] We are taught to believe that the earth

---

[121] Dr. Henry Morris, *Scientific Creationism*, p. 136.
[122] An in-depth study of the lies and consequences of evolution is Ken Ham's book, *The Lie: Evolution* (El Cajon, CA: Master Books, 1987).

is very old even though there is no <u>factual</u> science (see Chapter 2 "assumptions") to support eons of time. But we are not taught the bountiful evidences that lead to the conclusion that the earth is quite possibly only a few thousand years old. Textbook writers hold back and do not print the evidences for a young universe because they suppress the truth in unrighteousness (Romans 1:18).

How many evidences for a young earth can you list right now? Did you try to think of some? Can you write down even one solid proof that the earth is young? Most people (including Christians) cannot think of even one proof of a young age for the earth. You see! We have been led into one of the lies of Satan's world system—that the universe is very old.[123]

If a group of Christians were asked, "Do you believe God created the heavens and the earth?" Every hand would go up attesting to their sure belief, "Yes, God created the heavens and the earth." Should a second question be proposed, "Do you believe God used billions of years of geologic ages and the process of evolution to create?" Some pauses and waffling would occur, and if everyone were being honest, many hands would go up. Now, a third question is in order, "Do you believe that God created the heavens and the earth, the sea and all that is in them in a literal six 24-hour day week about 6,000 years ago?" In one evangelical church in Dallas, Texas, only five hands went up in a class of fifty people. You say, "They must not have understood the question!" No, they understood, but only five believed what the Bible says in Genesis 1-11, Exodus 20, John 1, Colossians 1, Hebrews 1, Revelation 4:11, etc. They had been brainwashed by Satan's

---

[123] For the most up to date information about the age of the earth from a creationist's position, read *Radioisotopes and the Age of the Earth*, edited by Larry Vardiman, Andrew A. Snelling and Eugene F. Chaffin (El Cajon, CA: Institute for Creation Research), 2000.

world system into thinking there is plenty of scientific evidence to prove an old, old universe.

Even in our conservative, evangelical churches there is little or no teaching regarding the creation issue. Let's face it, we have been more influenced by the worldly culture around us than we have penetrated culture with biblical Truth. We have become "conformed to this world" rather than being "transformed by the renewing" of our minds (Romans 12:2).

Dr. John C. Whitcomb has done us all a great service with his book, *The Early Earth: Revised Edition.* Dr. Whitcomb lists and discusses many of the evidences for believing the Bible to be true as written. He contrasts faith in God and His Word to faith in evolution and an old earth:

> ...the non-Christian scientist must acknowledge that *he also* comes to the factual, observable phenomenon with a set of basic assumptions and presuppositions that reflect a profound "faith-commitment." No scientist in the world today was present when the earth came into existence, nor do any of us have the privilege of watching worlds being created today! Therefore, the testimony of an honest evolutionist could be expressed in terms of...Hebrews 11:3..., as follows: "By faith, I, an evolutionist, understand that the worlds were *not* framed by the word of any god, so that what is seen has indeed been made out of previously existing and less complex visible things, by purely natural processes, through billions of years." Thus it is not a matter of the *facts* of science versus the *faith* of Christians! The fundamental issue, in the matter of ultimate origins, is whether one puts his trust in the written Word of the personal and living God who *was* there when it all happened, or else puts his trust in the ability of the human intellect, unaided by divine revelation to extrapolate presently observed processes of nature in the eternal past (and future). *Which faith* is the most reasonable, fruitful and satisfying? In my own case, while studying historical geology and paleontology at Princeton University, I was totally committed to evolutionary perspectives. Since then, however, I have discovered the biblical concept of ultimate origins to be far more satisfying in every respect.

Christians, who truly desire to honor God in their thinking, must not come to the first Chapter of Genesis with preconceived ideas of what could or could not have happened (in terms of current and changing concepts of uniformitarian scientism). *We are not God's counselors; He is ours! 'For who has known the mind of the Lord, or who became His counselor?'* (Romans 11:34) '...For my thoughts are not your thoughts, neither are your ways my ways, saith the Lord. For as the heavens are higher than the earth, so are my ways higher than your ways, and my thoughts than your thoughts' (Isa. 55:8-9).[124]

Do we know what we believe as Christians? Are we ready always to give an answer to every man who asks us to give an account of the hope that is within us (1 Peter 3:15)? As my wife and I travel around the USA, we are increasingly alarmed at the accelerating rate of departure from belief in a young earth and global Flood among the leadership of the church. Often, church leaders do not seem to realize the importance of Genesis 1-11 and the creation events as the foundation of our New Testament doctrine. Theistic evolution and progressive creationism have penetrated the church and almost no one in leadership has sounded the alarm. How can you have Christ the Lord as the last Adam if there was never a first Adam who began life in a sinless state and then fell (1 Corinthians 15:45)? How can there be a doctrine of sin with death as its penalty if there were all kinds of creatures dying as they eventually evolved into Adam? Why do we wear clothes (Genesis 3:21)? Where do we get the idea of one man, one woman as husband and wife for life (Genesis 2:21-25)? Why do we have human government (Genesis 9:1-7)? You see, the end result of not believing in a literal Genesis is murder, divorce, nudity, anarchy, etc., etc. Why do we see such horrible crime today? As Alexander Solzenitzen said, "We have forgotten God." How does a country forget God? It

---

[124] Dr. John C. Whitcomb, *The Early Earth: Revised Edition* (Grand Rapids: Baker Book House, 1986), p. 52.

begins by drifting away from a literal belief in the early, foundational chapters of Genesis (Jeremiah 2:32, 3:21; Ezekiel 23:35; Hosea 13:6, 4:6b)!

As a Christian leader, it is a good idea once in a while to review Scriptures such as Isaiah 9:16; Jeremiah 23:1, 50:6; Micah 3:5. The gospel begins with the Creator. The Creator reveals Himself to His creation in full power in early Genesis. Later, this same literal Genesis Creator, the Lord Jesus Christ (John 1; Colossians 1; Hebrews 1), entered His creation to die and be resurrected for the salvation of the fallen race of the first Adam! The span of time from Genesis chapter 1 until Jesus was about 4,000 years. Add 2,000 more years to get us up to the present, and the lifetime of planet earth is right at 6,000 years. There is absolutely no way to squeeze millions of years out of (or into) the Biblical text!!!

IS EARTH 6 THOUSAND OR 4.5 BILLION YEARS OLD?

How divergent are these two views (creation and a young earth versus evolution and an old earth)? Many evolutionists (and some creationists, such as Hugh Ross)[125] put the

---

[125] Hugh Ross wrote a book in 1994 entitled, *Creation and Time: A Biblical and Scientific Perspective on the Creation-Date Controversy*. This book was published by the Navigator's publishing arm, NavPress, and supports a billions-of-years old universe. Ross believes that people who teach a young earth perspective are keeping educated scientists from coming to faith in Jesus Christ as their Savior. With this position, Ross denies the sovereignty of Almighty God who will not lose one of His elect. Oddly, *The Presbyterian Layman* (Sept./Oct., 1994) agrees with Ross and states in the words of Alexander Metherell, M.D., Ph.D. (an elder in St. Andrew's Presbyterian Church, Newport Beach, Calif.), "Unfortunately, young earth creationists are resisting...with all their strength, fearful that the old earth view opens the door to evolution. In the process, they are placing in the way of educated unbelievers a stumbling block that keeps some from accepting Jesus Christ as their Lord and Savior." For an excellent critique of Hugh Ross' book which clearly displays misinterpretations of scientific theory and his errors in the exegesis of the Hebrew text, please read: *Creation and Time: A Report on the Progressive Creationist Book of Hugh Ross*, written by Mark Van Bebber and Paul Taylor [Eden Productions, 2628 West Birchwood Circle, Mesa, Arizona 85202. Phone: (800) 332-2261 or (602) 894-1300. Email: 71742.2074@compuserve.com].

beginning of earth at about 4.5 billion years ago. The Bible places The Beginning at about 6,000 years ago. Dennis Peterson attempts to help us understand the degree of difference in these two choices of faith:

> One way to visualize the extremes of our choices is to equate one year to the thinness of one page from a typical Bible. If you were to stack up several Bibles to a height about equal with your knee, you'd have about 6,000 pages before you.
>
> Now how many Bibles would you have to stack up to make four and a half billion pages?
>
> The stack would reach at least a hundred and fourteen miles high, above the stratosphere.
>
> So, you're standing there between your two stacks, and you are supposed to choose which one to believe in. Why is it you are made to feel rather sheepish to admit that you lean toward the Biblical stack of about 6,000 years? Or why is it that you start to arrogantly ridicule anyone who would dare to not agree with your proud billions?[126]

Petersen lists 35 or 40 evidences for a young earth. These are scientific reasons to believe the universe to be quite young— on the order of several thousand rather than several billion years. Petersen states:

> Scientists are aware of over 70 methods that can give us ideas of Earth's age. We could call these "GEOLOGIC CLOCKS." All of them are based on the obvious reality that natural processes occurring steadily through time produce cumulative and often measurable results. Most of these "clocks" give a relatively young age for the Earth. Only a few of them yield a conclusion of billions of years. Those few are loudly publicized to support the commonly held theory of gradualism.[127]

---

126 Petersen, *Unlocking the Mysteries of Creation*, Vol. I, p. 34.

127 Ibid., Petersen, p. 35.

THE POYNTING-ROBERTSON EFFECT

The gravitational fields of the sun and stars pull cosmic dust of certain kinds toward them (and certain particles are driven away, also). This is known as the Poynting-Robertson effect. Our sun is estimated to suck in about 100,000 tons of cosmic dust every day. An old sun should have "pulled in" and destroyed a significant number of particles in our solar system. Yet, our solar system is full of these particles! The Poynting-Robertson effect would seem to suggest a sun and solar system of less then 10,000 years of age.[128] Petersen states:

> All stars have a gravitational field and pull in particles like gas, dust and meteors within their range. Stars radiating energy 100,000 times faster than our sun have a spiraling effect, pulling things in all the faster. The unusual thing is that O and B stars are observed to have huge dust clouds surrounding them. If they were very old at all, every particle in close range would have been pulled in by now.[129]

Two types of stars, O and B, have huge dust clouds and, hence, must be quite young. No one has ever seen the birth of a new star, although some scientists have postulated through computer simulations and theoretical mathematics that as many as three new stars should form every year. No scientist ever has, nor ever will see a star form because the Creator created all of His stars on the fourth day of the creation week (Genesis 1:14-19).

In the spring of 1992, some scientists claimed to be observing a star form out in the stellar heavens. They used various mathematical equations to come to their conclusion. However, if their conclusion is in direct contradiction to what

---

[128] For more about the Poynting Robertson phenomenon, see: R.L. Wysong, *The Creation- Evolution Controversy* (Midland, Mich: Inquiry Press, 1981), p. 454ff. Also: Scott Huse, *The Collapse of Evolution* (Baker Books, 1983), p. 29.

[129] Ibid., Petersen, p. 44.

the Bible says, then their conclusion is wrong. Again, in 1995, the claim was made that the Hubble Space Telescope had found an immense, six trillion mile long, gaseous cloud that was a star incubator. The NASA picture displayed finger-like projections with stars in front, behind and imbedded in the cloud. Do stars in and around a cloud, in far outer space, prove that the cloud is making the stars? I don't think so.

So, we sit back and wait a few months or years and finally some scientist will sheepishly admit, "We are sorry folks, all our meticulously produced, computer enhanced evidence led us to believe a new star was forming, but we now realize that we made a mistake. We will keep looking for a new star to form and we will let you know as soon as we find it." God created His last star out of nothing on the fourth day of the creation week!

> **Lift up your eyes on high, and behold who hath created these things ["stars," NASB] that bringeth out their host by number: he calleth them all by names by the greatness of his might, for that he is strong in power; not one faileth ["not one of them is missing," NASB] (Isaiah 40:26).**

According to Isaiah, God made all the stars and has a name for each one. Astronomers may see stars die since sin entered the universe, but no star-birth is possible; God completed His creation of the universe and rested on the seventh day.

LIGHT FROM THE FARTHEST STARS

You might be thinking, "Okay, but what about the speed of light and the millions of years necessary to get light from the farthest stars to our solar system?" (This is one of the things I was thinking as I was "evolving" into a creationist back in the early seventies.) Well, first of all, how do we know it takes millions of years for light to travel to earth from the farthest stars? Some evolutionary professor told us, or some writer told us, or someone like Walter Cronkite or Dan Rather or Carl Sagan told us. There does seem to be a problem here, doesn't there?

Many scientists, evolutionists and creationists, are studying Russell Humphrys' ideas in his book, *Starlight and Time*.[130] To catch up on the recent developments in the time it takes starlight to reach planet earth from the farthest stars, Humphrys' book is a must. Perhaps it is "time" that varies. Humphrys discusses the effects of gravity on time. Even here on earth the atomic clock at Greenwich keeps time at a different rate than the atomic clock at the higher elevation at Boulder, Colorado. In outer space where the effects of gravity are much weaker than here on earth, the speed of light might remain constant, but time would be stretched out. With this effect, maybe one day on earth would be the same as one billion years in outer space! These ideas are out of my league, so I have to take other Christian creationists' endorsements of Humphrys' work.

What if you were to discover that light from the farthest star could arrive at earth instantly? God created the stars and at the same time the light beams from the stars to the earth. We can't eliminate this possibility. Our God could do this if He wanted to. He created a light beam and it didn't even have a material light source (the sun) behind it for the first three days of His creation week!

Look what finite man has done by God's grace: large files are transferred from computer to computer or computer to other devices (printer, palm pilots, etc) by infrared communication (without cables) in an incredibly short time. If finite man can do this, it should not be difficult to imagine what our infinite God can do. He created the vast stellar

---

[130] See the writings of Dr. Russell Humphreys at www.ICR.org.

universe and the light shining between all the things it contains, instantly.

Having said the above, even today, the distance to these remote stars has not been calculated. The methods used to measure great distances in space are closely examined in conjunction with the basic assumptions of Trigonometry. The actual distances in space may very well be as great as we have been told or they may not. The size of our universe surely appears to be vast, but we are here questioning the validity of the measuring techniques.

Measurements in space are arrived at by three commonly accepted techniques. The most reliable way to find out how far away an object is in space is to get into your spacecraft and fly to it, measuring the distance as you go.

A second way would be to shoot a laser beam and bounce it off of the surface of the object (a planet or the moon or an asteroid). The time it takes the light to go to the object and to come back tells you the distance. Most stars are too far away to use this method.

The third method is called "parallaxing." In this method, the extreme ends of earth's orbit can be used to triangulate. Most stars are so far away that it becomes impossible to make useful measurements of the angles to determine the apex of the triangle: the two sides of the triangle are almost parallel to each other. And the triangle gets to be too "skinny" as the apex ends up in the deep outer space. We cannot get into a space ship and travel to the stars to measure the distance, the laser beam technique has its limits and the triangulation method is only good for a distance of a few light years.

Anything beyond these three methods (and other methods, if any), is theoretical and a postulation. One such postulation is Doppler shift. This has not been reliable because the red shift and the blue shift of some stars have not been the absolute indication of their distances or directions of motion. Some astronomers now say that the red shift is not due to the Doppler effect at all. The supposed expansion of the universe is now believed to be an expansion of time and space. The space between galaxies is said to be increasing.

Another consideration is that light may have taken a "shortcut" through space. Different types of mathematics and different assumptions and postulates give totally different concepts of space and distances in space. What we know about space is quite limited. How distances through space are calculated depends on the calculator's system of math and his or her basic set of postulates (assumptions).

Outer space may be straight or it may be curved. If you like to think outer space is a straight line, you will use Euclidean Geometry and its accompanying assumptions. Euclidean Geometry is used to find vast distances in space. Its calculations are, for the most part, straight-line calculations. But, what if outer space is not able to be measured with straight-line from here-to-there-type math? That would mean all the farthest stars could be much closer than the textbooks teach.

NON-EUCLIDEAN GEOMETRY

There is still another alternative. Another legitimate way to measure distances in outer space is by using Riemannian math. Riemannian math is classified as Non-Euclidean Geometry. It assumes outer space to be curved. Hence Non-Euclidean Geometry produces much smaller distances to the farthest stars. Niessen (*ICR Impact* #121) reviewed articles by Harold Slusher ("Age of the Cosmos," I.C.R. 1980) and Wayne Zage ("The Geometry of Binocular Visual Space," *Mathematics Magazine* 53, Nov. 1980, pp. 289-293). Twenty-seven binary star systems were observed, and it appears that light travels in curved paths in deep space. If you convert Euclidean straight-line math into Riemannian curved math, light could travel from the farthest stars to earth in, as reported by Niessen, 15.71 years! This is a whole lot less than millions of years, isn't it?

Is Riemannian Geometry valid if it shows shorter distances to the stars? H.S.M. Coxeter published a largely ignored book in 1942 entitled *Non-Euclidean Geometry*. Coxeter stated, "...we still can't decide whether the real world is approximately Euclidean or approximately non-Euclidean."[131] The scientists do not know which is the valid way to measure space as it really is! They are not sure just what outer space really looks like. They have not been there and do not know what shape it has. Everything close enough to our solar system to obtain measurements (though all these contain assumptions) appears to have positive curvature. That means Riemann's method of figuring distance in space is more likely to be correct than the Euclidean methods. Niessen, then, has a chance of being correct when he postulates 15.71 years for light from the farthest star to reach

---

[131] "The full recognition that spherical geometry is itself a kind of non-Euclidean geometry, without parallels, is due to Riemann (1826-1866). He realized that Saccheri's hypothesis of the obtuse angle becomes valid as soon as Postulates I, II, and V are modified to read:

I.   *Any two points determine at least one line.*
II. *A line is unbounded.*
V.   *Any two lines in a plane will meet.*

For a line to be unbounded and yet of finite length, it merely has to be re-entrant, like a circle. The great circles on a sphere provide a model for the finite lines on a finite plane, and, when so interpreted, satisfy the modified postulates. But if a line and a plane can each be finite and yet unbounded, why not also an n-dimensional manifold, and in particular the three-dimensional space of the real world? In Riemann's words of 1854: "The unboundedness of space possesses a greater empirical certainty than any external experience. But its infinite extent by no means follows from this; on the other hand, if we assume independence of bodies from position, and therefore ascribe to space constant curvature, it must necessarily be finite provided this curvature has ever so small a positive value."

According to the General Theory of Relativity, astronomical space has positive curvature locally (wherever there is matter), but we cannot tell whether the curvature of "empty" space is exactly zero or has a very small positive or negative value. In other words, we still cannot decide whether the real world is approximately Euclidean or approximately non-Euclidean." H. S. M. Coxeter, *Non-Euclidean Geometry*, 5th ed. (Canada: University of Toronto Press, 1965), pp. 11,12.

planet earth. And if the speed of light has not been constant since the Beginning, this might also get light to earth much more quickly. Scientists recently increased the speed of light to 300 times its normal speed by passing it through a Caesium chamber.

Let us not forget what Jeremiah, the prophet of God, said:

He hath made the earth by his power, he hath established the world by his wisdom, and hath stretched out the heavens by his discretion (Jeremiah 10:12).

Perhaps God made the stars closer to earth with their light already here and then he moved the stars away by "stretching out" the heavens. So instead of the star being made after the Big Bang way out in space, and us having to wait for millions of years for its light to get here, God made it closer to earth with its light already here and then moved the star away to its place out in space. I believe Humphrys asserts that the "stretching out" of the heaven could have taken place on the fourth day.

If world class physicist, Paul Davies, is correct in his article in *Nature* [Davies, P.C.W., and Lineweaver, C.H., "Black Holes Constrain Varying Constants," *Nature* 418 (6896): 602-603, August 8, 2002] that contends that the speed of light has quite possibly been slowing down, then, if the speed of light has not been constant, the universe may be quite young! Millions of years of age for stars, and the idea that these stars are millions of miles away is calculated under the assumption that the speed of light has always been the same. The most recent research indicates that time and the speed of light are NOT CONSTANTS!

What conclusion can we arrive at on the basis of all the above? You do not have to believe it when some textbook or scientist in a white lab coat tells you that stars are millions of light-years and perhaps trillions of miles away. There is no hard, irrefutable evidence here for a 9 to 20 billion year old universe. Those stars could very well be billions of light years away. Our Lord has shown us by creating Adam, Eve, trees, animals, etc., fully mature that he can create a star with a fully mature light beam that comes to earth no matter how far away that star might be. <u>Perhaps the time to get here is speeded up in outer space, and the speed of light is faster in days gone by</u>!

Where do the 9 to 20 billion years come from? Hubble came up with the theoretical, mathematical formula for measuring time back to the initial "Big Bang." His calculations originally estimated about 18 to 20 billion years as the age of the universe. Then, a few years ago, some other scientists decided Hubble had made a grievous mistake and was 50% off in his calculations. Thus, the age of the universe was cut in half (from 18 to 20 billion years to 9 to 10 billion years) by the stroke of a pen. Some scientists still hold to the 20 billion year figure. They realize that even 20 billion years is statistically not long enough to evolve the universe and all the diversity it contains.

COMBUSTION ENERGY OF STARS

Now, back to some more evidences for a young universe. Astronomers calculate that certain types of stars may have surface temperatures of 90,000°F. This is "... more than 100,000 times the energy coming from our sun. Burning down at that rate, and clocking backward, the entire universe would have been filled with the mass of these stars just a few thousand years ago!"[132]

Some evolutionists will object, "But you can't take current processes and extrapolate back like that." Well, what do evolutionists do to find and publish their old, old dates? The same thing! They evaluate, for example, present processes such as decay rates (½ life), speed of light etc. and

---

132 Petersen, p. 44.

extrapolate backwards assuming all was the same from the beginning (2 Peter, Chapter 3, explains to us that all is NOT the same from the Beginning—that there was one kind of heaven/earth system before the Flood and another kind of heaven/earth after the Flood).

BRISTLE-CONE PINE TREES

If the Biblical Flood occurred about 4,500 years ago and destroyed all dry-land plant life, then we would not expect to find plants that could be accurately dated at older than about 4,500 years. The bristle-cone pine tree is such a plant. It has been called the oldest living organism on earth and has been dated at about 5,000 years. Peterson states, "It's almost as though all these trees were planted on a virgin Earth just 5,000 years ago."[133]

Just because a tree has 5,000 rings it does not necessarily mean that the tree is 5,000 years old. For the last three years, at our home in Texas, our trees have had two rings each year. We had a wet spring and then no rain for two and a half months. The trees went initially dormant, and then, with the autumn rains, the Bradford Pear trees came out of dormancy and began to bloom again. This gave them two sets of rings in one year. Bristle-cone pines are very old, but less than 5,000 years!

RIVERS ARE YOUNG

Every year the Mississippi River carries tons and tons of eroded dirt into the Gulf of Mexico. Scientists have been measuring the growth of the Mississippi delta for many years.

At the present rate the entire Mississippi River delta would have accumulated in only 5,000 years. But science acknowledges that the river has been even bigger in the past.

---

[133] Ibid., p. 38.

How could this be? Unless of course the North American continent, and all the other continents for that matter, just haven't been in their present positions any longer than that.[134]

Another river that scientists carefully watch is the Niagara. It also leads to belief in a young earth.

Because the rim of the falls is wearing back at a known rate every year, geologists recognize that is has only taken about 5,000 years to erode from its original precipice.[135]

Some measurements have indicated 25,000 years of erosion at pre-hydroelectric rates, while others mention a buried canyon that would require another 10,000 years. All of these figures assume a constant amount of water and a steady rate of erosion. But, after observing the catastrophe of Mount St Helens, we know that the initial run off of the Flood slurry waters could carve a deep canyon in a matter of hours or days. Often large chunks of the dirt and rock under waterfalls, like the Niagara, will break off, yielding even younger ages. Suppose that 200 years from now you decided to calculate the age of Niagara Falls, but you did not know that in 2002 a huge section of rock had broken away from the edge of the falls. You would assume that it took thousands of years to wear away all that rock from the falls' edge, but it happened in an instant. You would date the falls much older than it actually was. This type of mistake is common when scientists attempt to date things.

THE RECEDING MOON

Adding to the evidence for a young earth is our receding moon. Scientists know how fast our moon is moving away from earth (about two inches per year).

---

[134] Ibid., p. 38.
[135] Ibid., p. 39.

Louis B. Slichter, Professor of Geophysics at M.I.T., writes:

> The time scale of the earth-moon system still presents a major problem.[136]

Dennis Petersen continues:

> ...working it back would mean the moon and Earth would be touching only two billion years ago. Of course, that's ridiculous. Another way to look at it is this: At the present rate and starting from a realistic distance of separation between the two, if the Earth is five billion years old the moon should be out of sight by now![137]

New ideas are constantly being presented about the origin of our moon, such as our moon arose because of a collision between planet earth and a planetesimal. As creationists, we need to be aware of new ideas, but always subject them to the Bible. The Bible says:

> **And God made two great lights: the greater light to rule the day, and the lesser light to rule the night; he made the stars also (Genesis 1:16).**

God says he made the moon on the same day he made the sun, the fourth day of the creation week. He doesn't tell us that he made the moon by means of some collision with a planetesimal like the latest theories claim.

MOON ROCKS

When the first moon rocks were dated in the early 1970's, NASA published the age of the moon rocks at 4 to 4.5 billion years. Several years and many rocks later, they published a

---

[136] Louis B. Slichter, "Secular Effects of Tidal Friction upon the Earth's Rotation," *Journal of Geophysical Research*, Vol. 8 No. 14 (1964), 4281-4288.

[137] Petersen, p. 43.

range of dates for the rocks of our moon at 3 to 4.5 billion years. This author called one of the geologists who dated those rocks and the conversation went something like this:

> "I noticed in a recent news release that the dates of the moon rocks have been adjusted to a range of 1.5 billion years. That's a pretty big difference in the dates! Was the range any greater than that?"
>
> "Oh yes, the range went from several thousand years to over 20 billion years."
>
> "Well then, why did NASA only publish the 1.5 billion year range, instead of the full 20+ billion year range?"
>
> "We did not want to confuse the public. We know the moon is about 3 to 4.5 billion years old, so we called the dates outside of that range discordant dates and threw them out."

"Assumptions determine conclusions" and some scientists must have pre-decided (assumed) that the moon is about 3 to 4.5 billion years old before any rocks were ever brought back from the moon. What if, in spite of their presuppositional belief, the several thousand year dates were correct and not discordant? Well, that locks in Special Creation and eliminates the possibility of evolution that requires millions of years. Apparently that was unacceptable to NASA thirty years ago.

Or, what if the 20+ billion years dates were correct? That, in effect, demolishes Hubble's math, and the time of the Big Bang is once again up for grabs. These scientists might object and say, "But we use a bell-shaped curve to arrive at our dates." Well, what if the assumptions, which are built into their dating system, skew the curve one way or another? We've already seen that the three major assumptions invariably included when scientists date rocks are not valid.

You might ask an astronomer where our moon and its rocks came from. Some fanciful answers will be forthcoming! Evolutionary scientists do not know from whence cometh our moon. A creationist believes that the God of the Bible created the moon, and the sun and stars as well, on the fourth day of the creation week (Genesis 1:14-19). There is no hard, factual, scientific information that can refute a young age for the moon. All old ages given for the moon are not accurate because the assumptions behind the dating techniques are not realistic.

SHORT-TERM COMETS

From time to time, comets pass by the earth. Not only can scientists not tell us where our moon came from, they also cannot tell us about the origin of short-term comets. These are comets that astronomers calculate have lifetimes of no more than 100,000 years. If the universe is somewhere between 9 and 20 billion years old, and the astral bodies were formed as the result of the "Big Bang," evolution is left in the embarrassing dilemma of having to postulate theories for the origin of short-term comets, which it cannot prove. You have to admire the imagination of these folks, though. Some actually believe that Jupiter spits comets out of high volcanoes. The only problem is that the short-lived comets are not made of the right stuff to even come from Jupiter, and their orbit is in no way oriented to enable them to refer to Jupiter as "mother." Scott Huse says:

> Comets journey around the sun and are assumed to be the same age as the solar system. Each time a comet orbits the sun, a small part of its mass is 'boiled off.' Careful studies indicate that the effect of this dissolution process on short-term comets would have totally dissipated them in about 10,000 years. Based on the fact that there are still numerous comets orbiting the sun with no source of new comets known to exist, we can deduce that our solar system cannot be much older than 10,000 years. To date, no satisfactory explanation has been given to discredit this evidence for a youthful solar system.[138]

---

[138] Huse, *The Collapse of Evolution*, pp. 28, 29.

One idea for these young comets is that there is something called an "Oort cloud" out beyond Pluto's orbit that generates comets (not yet seen). Another guess is that as stars pass by they "kick" comets into our solar system. I choose to stick with the Bible. God made the contents of the heavens on the fourth day about 6,000 years ago!

EARTH'S MAGNETIC FIELD

An examination of the Earth's magnetic field suggests that Earth cannot be very old, since the Earth's magnetic field is losing its strength. Dr. Thomas Barnes has done volumes of work on the depletion of Earth's magnetic field. The conclusion of his work establishes the age of the Earth at less than 10,000 years.[139] Naturally, the evolutionary community has proclaimed Barnes' work invalid, but Barnes answers their charges quite simply and effectively in the *ICR Impact* #122, August 1983, entitled "Earth's Magnetic Age: The Achilles Heel of Evolution." The earth's magnetic field is getting measurably weaker. Ten thousand years ago it would have been too strong to support life. If life could not have existed 10,000 years ago because of the super strength of the earth's magnetic field, then evolution had no time to occur.

Some objections have arisen about Barnes' work. Geologic processes seem to indicate earth's magnetic field may have reversed rapidly many times in the past. Dr. John Baumgardner has suggested that during the cataclysmic tectonic movements of earth during the Flood, earth's magnetism was unstable.[140]

---

[139] For more see: "Origin and Destiny of the Earth's Magnetic Field," T.G. Barnes, *I.C.R. Technical Monograph* No. 4, 1973; also *ICR Impact* #100, October 1981.

[140] For further reading you might begin with J. R. Baumgardner, "The Imperative of Non-Stationary Natural Law in Relation to Noah's Flood," *Creation Research Society Quarterly* 27:3(1990) 98-100.

It seems to me that we must believe magnetism to be stable (allowing for slow entropy) since shortly <u>after</u> the Flood. If earth's magnetic pole is constantly moving around and gaining and losing strength, there arises a huge problem. How does the Pacific Golden Plover navigate from Alaska to Hawaii over 4,000 miles of ocean water with no landmarks? How does the Humpback whale find its way from the Arctic to the equatorial seas? Magnetite has been found in the Humpback and many researchers have reached a consensus that these and many other migratory creatures utilize earth's magnetism as their guidance system. If earth's magnetism were fickle, then we would have many migratory animals completely lost! But if earth's magnetism were unstable during The Flood (or some point prior to The Flood), it would certainly interfere with an evolutionary view that these animals gradually established their migratory routes.

As Dr. Russell Humphreys states: "...the earth's magnetic field certainly is less than 100,000 years old; very likely less than 10,000 years old, and fits in well with the face-value biblical age of 6,000 years" (See www.icr.org/pubs/imp/imp-242.htm).

OUR SHRINKING SUN

Recently, a controversy has arisen over the shrinking of our sun. If the figures of John Eddy and Adam Boornazian are correct ("Analysis of Historical Data Suggest the Sun is Shrinking," *Physics Today*, Vol. 32 No. 9, September 1979), our sun would have been too hot for life to exist on Earth even 1,000,000 years ago. This would, in effect, knock out the possibility of the vast expanses of time required for evolution. Evolutionists and theistic evolutionists have jumped on this one to prove Eddy was mistaken. Others now claim that the measurements of the sun (measured when the planet Mercury crosses in front of the sun each year) prove the size of the sun has not changed. We will have to wait to see how this develops.[141]

In any event, there is a growing body of evidence that our sun is quite young! According to *ICR Impact* #276 (www.icr.org/pubs/imp/imp-276.htm), evidences for a young sun include: The fundamental oscillation of the sun matches the model for a young sun, the solar neutrino emission is that of a young sun and the lithium and beryllium abundance in the sun is consistent with that of a young sun. This evidence in no way surprises a young earth creationist, since we know that the Creator God of the Bible created the sun, moon and stars with their useful and necessary relationships to planet earth about 6,000 years ago. For more about the sun and gravitational collapse as opposed to thermonuclear reactions, read p. 58-61 in Dr. Theodore Rybka's book, *Geophysical and Astronomical Clocks*.[142] In the back, he has some tables listing <u>maximum</u> possible ages for things such as: dispersion of meteor showers—10,000 years; rings of Saturn—114,000 years; dust in interplanetary space—10,000,000 years; bridges between quasars—7000 years; fast burn rate of hot stars—100,000 years; etc. He lists many more evidences that require a universe much younger than billions of years!

RADIOHALOS

Support for a young earth is offered by Robert V. Gentry through his studies of radiohalos (little halos that surround a speck of radioactive material) in coalified wood.

---

[141] Science Held Hostage is a book by three men from Calvin College who appear to be theistic evolutionists. They do not believe in a young earth. The "evolution/creation in six days" controversy is not an issue to cause the elect to lose fellowship with each other [Howard J. Van Till, Davis A. Young and Clarence Menninga, *Science Held Hostage* (Downers Grove, Ill: Inter Varsity Press, 1988)].

[142] Dr. Theodore Rybka in his book, *Geophysical and Astronomical Clocks* (Irvine, CA: American Writing and Publishing Co., 1993), refutes the arguments of Hugh Ross and Van Till, Young and Menninga by showing that the sun's heat is generated by gravitational collapse and not nuclear fusion.

Evolutionists believe the coal deposits in the Colorado Plateau to be hundreds of millions of years old. Yet, Gentry's radio-halo "clock" suggests a time period of only a few thousand years.[143] Gentry discovered microscopic bits of uranium in these coal deposits. The effect of the radioactive uranium on the coal was to produce radiation halos in the coal.

Paul Ackerman comments on Gentry's radiohalo work:

> As a radioactive bit decays, radiation extends in all directions into surrounding coal for a small, yet precise distance determined by the particle energy of the radiation. Over time this emitted radiation will change the color of the coal, forming a distinct sphere around the bit of uranium in the center. These tiny spheres of discolored rock surrounding a microscopic radioactive center are termed "radiohalos." Such radiohalos are Robert Gentry's specialty.[144]

How does the bit of radioactive uranium get into the coal to form the halos? Ackerman continues:

> Regarding the radioactive center, a bit of uranium has, at some time in the past, before the wood material was hardened into coal, migrated into its present position. As the uranium bit undergoes radioactive decay, a form of lead is created. Once the coal has hardened and the uranium bit has been cemented into a fixed position, this lead isotope begins to accumulate at the site....
>
> Gentry has found that the uranium/lead ratios in the Colorado Plateau coal formation indicate that this formation is only a few thousand years old.[145]

The halos form around the radioactive particles in the coal and indicate a young age of only a few thousand years for the

---

[143] Robert V. Gentry, et al., "Radiohalos in Coalified Wood: New Evidence Relating to the Time of Uranium Introduction and Coalification," *Science*, 194 (October 15, 1976), 315-317.

[144] Paul D. Ackerman, *It's a Young World After All: Exciting Evidences for Recent Creation* (Grand Rapids: Baker Book House, 1986), pp. 104, 105.

[145] Ibid., Ackerman, P. 105.

coal. The coal of the Colorado Plateau was probably formed during the Flood judgment of Noah's day as God was destroying heaven-and-earth system #1. One type of Polonium has a short half-life of three minutes. Another type is measured in nanoseconds. For these bits of material to inscribe themselves in rock and coal with their characteristic "tattoos" something had to be happening with flash speed!

Gentry also found halos of Polonium in Precambrian granite rock. These are supposedly the oldest rocks on earth. Precambrian rock is called the "basement" rock of earth since it is thought to be more ancient than all other rock. Ackerman continues to review Gentry's work:

> The question Gentry has raised for evolutionists is how the polonium bits and their resulting halos came to be in the basement granites....
>
> The enigma is this: If the granite is hardened, the polonium cannot travel to its intrusion location. But if the granite is not hardened, no halo can form. Therefore, Gentry argues that the time lapse from a permeable, molten state to the present rock state for these precambrian granites had to be extremely brief. How brief? One of the polonium isotopes studies by Gentry has a half-life of three minutes! Another has a half-life of only 164 microseconds!
>
> In the evolutionary model, the time required for the cooling and solidification of these granites is millions and millions of years. Gentry believes these halos to constitute powerful evidence against evolution and its presumed vast time spans. He believes these halos speak of a very rapid formation of these crustal rocks.[146]

Radiohalos in Precambrian basement rock may indicate a young age for the earth's "oldest" rocks [for more read: *Radioisotopes and the Age of the Earth*, see footnote #123]. Walter T. Brown, Jr., (*In The Beginning*), lists about thirty time clocks for the age of the earth that yield an age of a few

---

[146] Ibid., Ackerman, pp. 108-110.

thousand years. He mentions that an analysis of the gases (such as helium) in the atmosphere yields a young age (few thousand years) for the age of the atmosphere.[147] Helium gas is found in deep, hot rocks. If these rocks were even one billion years old the helium would have escaped, but it is still retained in the rock. This means that the rock can be only a few thousand years old.[148]

RIVER SEDIMENTS

River sediments and erosion rates indicate that the earth could not have existed as it is for millions of years.[149] [See also: Dr. Henry Morris, *The Defender's Study Bible* (Grand Rapids: World Publishing, 1995), Appendix 5.]

PLANETARY RINGS

A study of the rings around several planets seems to demand a young age for our solar system:

> The rings that are orbiting Saturn, Uranus, Jupiter and Neptune are being rapidly bombarded by meteoroids. Saturn's rings, for example, should be pulverized and dispersed in about 10,000 years. Since this has not happened, planetary rings are probably quite young...
>
> Jupiter and Saturn each radiate more than twice the energy they receive from the sun. Venus also radiates too much energy. Calculations show it is very unlikely that this energy comes from nuclear fusion, radioactive decay, gravitational contraction or phase changes within those planets. The only other conceivable explanation is that these planets have not existed long enough to cool off.[150]

---

[147] Brown, *In the Beginning*, p. 16.

[148] See: R. V. Gentry, "Differential Helium Retention in Zircons" *Geophysical Research Letters* 9 (October 1982) pp. 1129-1130.

[149] Brown, p. 16.

[150] Brown, p. 18.

STAR CLUSTERS

The existence of star clusters hints at a young universe. Immense clusters of stars are traveling through space, we are told, at supersonic speeds. Scientists believe that gravity holds these fast moving star clusters together. But scientists do not know how these star clusters could hold together for millions of years, while traveling at such high speeds. They should have "unclustered" and moved apart by now, especially with the effects of entropy. But they are still in a cluster. The sole answer to this dilemma for the evolutionist appears to be special creation a few thousand years ago, not a "Big Bang" billions of years ago.

MOUNT ST. HELENS

When all other evidence fails to prove a very old heaven-and-earth system, evolutionists go back to rocks and rock formations, which supposedly require very long spans of time to form. The eruption of Mount St. Helens on May 18, 1980, and the rapid formation of geologic systems around it, is challenging the claims of historical geology. Dr. Steve Austin and Institute for Creation Research staff personnel have been documenting the phenomena of Mount St. Helens since its initial eruption. Some surprising results of the volcanic blast are being observed.

> Up to 600 feet thickness of strata have formed since 1980 at Mount St. Helens. These deposits accumulated from primary air blast, landslide, waves on the lake, pyroclastic flows, mud flows, air fall and stream water... Mount St. Helens teaches us that the stratified layers commonly characterizing geological formations can form very rapidly by flow processes.[151]

---

[151] Steven A. Austin, Ph.D., "Mount St. Helens and Catastrophism," *ICR Impact* #157, July 1986, p. 1, 2. Dr. Austin also has an excellent video on this topic.

In other words, what geologists may have thought took thousands or hundreds of thousands of years to form as a column of rock, in fact, formed at Mount St. Helens (as the scientists watched) in less than eleven years! Perhaps eons of time are not necessary to form the layers of rock after all.

One more fascinating phenomenon of the Mount St. Helens cataclysmic explosion is the apparent formation of the beginnings of polystrate fossils in five years. In 1985, scientists discovered that water-soaked trees were floating with root end down (toward the bottom of the lake) in Spirit Lake. These trees:

> ...are randomly spaced not clumped together, over the bottom of the lake, again having the appearance of being an in situ forest [a forest that grew there, Ed.].
>
> Scuba investigation of the upright deposited trunks shows that some are already solidly buried by sedimentation, with more than three feet of sediment around their bases. This proved that the upright trees were deposited at different times, with their roots buried at different levels. If found buried in the stratigraphic record (rocks), these trees might be interpreted as multiple forests which grew on different levels over periods of thousands of years. The Spirit Lake upright deposited stumps, therefore, have considerable implications for interpreting "petrified forests" in the stratigraphic record.[152]

What does this all mean? There is a bank of polystrata fossils (one tree goes up through several layers or strata of sedimentary rock) in Nova Scotia over 2,000 feet thick with trees straight up and down at different levels up through the rocks. Geologists have claimed that a formation like the Nova Scotia formation would take hundreds of thousands of years to form. After observing the Spirit Lake water-soaked trees, scientists are reconsidering. Perhaps it does not take as long as they originally thought to form polystrate fossils. Those

---

[152] Austin, *ICR Impact* #157, p. iii.

trees in Spirit Lake are lining up and getting buried in what should become sedimentary rock—but just a few years have gone by, not hundreds of thousands of years!

The Spirit Lake trees seem to be showing a fossil forest in production. An example of an existing fossil forest (similar to Spirit lake) is in Yellowstone National Park and is a popular tourist attraction. Based on observations of the Spirit lake upright trees, the Yellowstone fossil forest may be only a few thousand years old, not millions of years old as taught by the Park Service.

INSTANT PETROLEUM

On August 18, 1986, U.S. News and World Report stated: "Last year in the Gulf of California, MIT's Edmond found that the action of hot vents was turning dead plankton in the sediment into petroleum—a process that normally takes at least 10 million years squeezed into an instant." Obviously, it does not require millions of years to form oil if oil has been proven to form in an instant. Could it be that the earth is not as old as we have been told?

With so many observable evidences for a young earth, which can only be answered by an earth that once was greenhouse warm and suddenly (about the time of the Flood) became permanently frozen at the poles, why do evolutionists still cling to their old earth/local flood theories? Only one answer seems plausible: they do not want to submit themselves in humble obedience to their Creator. They refuse to accept the Lord Jesus Christ even though He reveals Himself through His creation. Evolution from one cell to man is a lie and a foolish speculation of men in rebellion against their Creator.

For the wrath of God is revealed from heaven against all ungodliness and unrighteousness of men, who hold the truth in unrighteousness;

Because that which may be known of God is manifest in them; for God hath shewed it unto them.

For the invisible things of him from the creation of the world are clearly seen, being understood by the things that are made, even his eternal power and divine Godhead; so that they are without excuse:

Because that, when they knew God, they glorified him not as God, neither were thankful; but became vain in their imaginations, and their foolish heart was darkened.

Professing themselves to be wise, they became fools. [Romans 1:18-22 (Emphasis added)].

He hath made the earth by his power,
He hath established the world by his wisdom,
And hath stretched out the heavens by his discretion
(Jeremiah 10:12).

MARVEL OF GOD'S CREATION

#9

The Chuckwalla Lizard

"Chuckwalla lizards are large, pot-bellied lizards which wear a loose, baggy skin. Though the skin appears to be much too large, it is just exactly what this lizard needs when an enemy approaches. You see, when an enemy comes near the chuckwalla, the lizard runs very quickly to a rock crevice and hides in it. In the crack of the rock, the chuckwalla swallows air and blows up like a balloon. When the enemy, arrives the chuckwalla is safely wedged in the crack. Though it is within easy reach, it is safe. Years ago, the Indians of our desert Southwest learned how to catch the chuckwalla. They pierced its body with an arrow to let out the air; then the Indians could easily remove the lizard from its haven. Man is probably the only enemy of the chuckwalla lizard from whom it is not completely safe.

Of course, the desert is very dry. Some chuckwallas live where there may be only a single rain shower in a whole year. In these arid places the chuckwalla generally lives a dormant life for most of the year. It estivates, or sleeps, for all but about five months of the year.

While living actively, the chuckwalla eats whatever juicy plants it can find. Special glands store the water from the greenery, and the chuckwalla grows fat from its food. Generally, chuckwallas are dormant from August through March.

Many desert plants absorb much salt from the soil in which they grow. The chuckwalla receives enough salt from its food to kill an ordinary animal. The salt would kill the chuckwalla, too, were it not for its special salt-removing glands. These glands are located in the nostrils of the chuckwalla, and, as the salt builds up on the glands, the lizard occasionally sneezes. The sneeze expels the crystallized salt which the glands have filtered out of the lizard's bloodstream.

The cold-blooded chuckwalla sleeps late. But when it arises, it must warm up in a hurry. Desert nights and early mornings are often very cold. Cold-blooded creatures are slow and sluggish when they are cold, and cold lizards are easy to catch. For this reason, the chuckwalla wears a dark-colored, heat-absorbing skin. The sun warms the lizard before the air warms up. Later in the day, the lizard's skin changes to a heat-reflecting light color because the chuckwalla must not get too hot either. The rationality we find when we examine the chuckwalla's body structure compels us to recognize its Designer. Only God, Who is an intelligent, rational Being, can account for the order and design evident in the chuckwalla lizard and all of nature."[153]

---

[153] DeWitt Steele, *Science: Order and Reality* (Pensacola, Fl: A Beka Book Publications, 1980), p. 138. Christian parents, do you realize that there are science books that your children can be studying that defend the creationist's perspective and support the teachings of the Bible?

10

DECEPTION IN THE TEXTBOOKS

A re there any fraudulent ideas promoted in the teachings and texts of the evolutionists? Jonathan Wells, Ph.D. (molecular and cell biology), from UC-Berkeley, lists a few of the known frauds in evolutionary teachings:

> We all remember them from biology class: the experiment that created the "building blocks of life" in a tube; the evolutionary "tree," rooted in the primordial slime and branching out into animal and plant life. Then there were the similar bone structures of, say, a bird's wing and a man's hand, the peppered moths, and Darwin's finches. And don't forget, Haeckel embryos.
>
> As it happens, all of these examples, as well as many others, purportedly standing as evidence of evolution, turn out to be incorrect. Not just slightly off. Not just slightly mistaken. On the subject of Darwinian evolution, the texts contained massive distortions and even faked evidence. Nor are we only talking about high-school textbooks that some might excuse (but shouldn't) for adhering to a lower standard. Also guilty are some of the most prestigious and widely used college texts, such as Douglas Futuyma's Evolutionary Biology, and the latest edition of the graduate-level textbook, Molecular Biology of the Cell, coauthored by the president of the National Academy of Sciences, Bruce Alberts. In fact, when the false "evidence" is taken away, the case for Darwinian evolution, in the textbooks at least, is so thin it's almost invisible.[154]

---

[154] Jonathan Wells, Ph.D., "Survival of the Fakest," *The American Spectator*, December 2000/January 2001, pp. 19-20. See also his book, *Icons of Evolution: Science or Myth* (Washington, D.C.: Regnery Publishing, 2000).

THE PEPPERED MOTH

The peppered moth is no longer believed to be an example of natural selection and evolution-in-progress even though it remains in most major textbooks. The idea presented in the textbooks is that during the Industrial Revolution, smoke and soot from the factories accumulated on the tree trunks where the peppered moths lived. Because of the ash on the tree trunks, the light colored moths were less visible to the birds, so the birds were eating more of the dark colored moths. This is taught to the students as an example of natural selection (one of the primary engines of evolution) in action. There were light and dark colored moths before, during and after the Industrial Revolution. The surprising truth is that the peppered moths never lived on tree trunks as pictured in our texts. Those pictures that display the moths on an ash-covered tree trunk, with the light moth barely visible and the dark moth sticking out like lunch for the nearest bird, are a fraud! Peppered moths do not even rest on tree trunks. Dead moths were glued to the tree trunk for the textbook pictures![155] These fraudulent texts are deceiving our children!

> But evil men and seducers shall wax worse and worse, deceiving and being deceived (2 Timothy 3:13).

ONTOGENY RECAPITULATES PHYLOGENY

Didn't we all learn that "ontogeny recapitulates phylogeny?" This is the idea that, for instance, the human embryo goes through a fish stage, reptile stage, etc., while developing in the mother's womb. Remember those science book pictures of the embryos of different creatures and they all looked alike as they developed in eggs or wombs? Well

---

[155] See *Creation ex Nihilo*, vol. 21, No.2, June-August 1999, p. 56; *The Washington Times*, January 17, 1999, p. D8; and *The Calgary Herald*, March 21, 1999, p. D3.

this may rankle you a bit, but those drawings of embryos were proven to be false in the 1880's![156] Ernst Haeckel was disciplined by his academic peers in the 1880's for adding and omitting features and fudging the scale "to exaggerate similarities among species." His drawings reduced the size of some embryos as much as ten times to make them look similar to other unrelated species.[157]

This Haeckel embryo FRAUD continues in our childrens' texts today with full knowledge of the text's authors and the professors and teachers who teach it! One such text at the college level is *Life, Fourth Edition* (copyright 2002). (Parents, this book is the Biology text at a "Christian" college. It teaches evolution as fact and equates creationism with astrology, extrasensory perception, fortune telling, healing crystals and psychic phenomena on page 10). This book deals with the Haeckel's drawings in such a way that after stating that Haeckel took "a bit of artistic license" and that his drawings "did not represent scale," it says, "The data show that there really are similarities in embryonic structures, supporting the concept of common ancestry."[158] This writer would agree that there are similarities in the external appearance of embryos a few hours to a few days old. How much difference can there be between one-cell, two-cell, four-cell, sixteen-cell, etc., embryos developing in such a way that they, even as totally different organisms, can share a common atmosphere and food chain?

Even the questions at the bottom of page 329 of *Life* bring the student's thinking back to the Haeckel idea. Question 4

---

[156] See: *New Scientist*, September 6, 1997, p.23; and *Science*, vol. 277, September 5, 1997.

[157] Also see: M. Richardson, et al., "There is no Highly Conserved Stage in the Vertebrates: Implications for Current Theories of Evolution and Development," *Anatomy and Embryology*, 1997, 196(2): 91-106.

[158] Ricki Lewis, Douglas Gaffin, Marielle Hoefnagels and Bruce Parker, *Life* (Boston: McGraw Hill, 2002), p.329.

reads: "Why do vertebrate embryos appear similar, but then become very different adult animals?" What is the answer the text writers are hoping the student will arrive at? Is it, "Embryos appear similar because they are embryologically retracing their evolutionary history as they develop?"

At the top of page 330 of *Life*, the student is again reminded of the similarities of embryos. Figure 17.13 is entitled "Embryo Resemblances." Figure 17.13 reproduces a set of Haeckel's drawings and a set of photographs of the actual embryos (The actual photographs were, I believe, produced by British embryologist, Dr. Michael Richardson in 1997, although *Life* does not reference the photographs).

There are two horizontal rows of pictures in the text. The top row of five different embryos (fish, salamander, chicken, rabbit and human) is the reproduced Richardson photographs. The second horizontal row is the Haeckel fraudulent drawings. There is very little resemblance between the photos and the drawings. Also, the text does not tell the student if the embryos of the different organisms are at different stages of development or that all embryos are at the same day and stage of development. The sizes of all the embryos are fairly equal in the text pictures, which also give the impression that embryos of rabbits and humans are not all that different!

If the textbook, *Life*, is truly attempting to dispel the myth of ontogeny recapitulates phylogeny as depicted in Haeckel's fraudulent drawings and still believed by many evolutionists, then Figure 17.13 is mislabeled. Instead of being entitled "Embryo Resemblances," it should be titled "Haeckel's Fraudulent Drawings Compared to the Real Embryos."

Even the explanatory paragraph of Figure 17.13 is misleading. The first sentence reads: "Vertebrate embryos appear alike early in development, reflecting the similarities of basic processes as cells divide and specialize, as the figure shows for five species." Well, the only embryos that look alike in Figure 17.13 are the reproduced Haeckel drawings, not the Richardson photographs of the real embryos! As a matter of fact, there is a ten-fold difference in the size of the salamander drawing of Haeckel compared to the photo of the real salamander as reported in *Science*, September 5, 1997. This huge difference in size is not pictured, nor is it mentioned in the *Life* textbook caption of Figure 17.13. The message that comes across in *Life* is that embryos are all pretty much alike and that is what we would expect since we all came from fish to amphibian to reptile to birds and mammals. When a person has on their "old universe" evolutionary worldview glasses it appears that they skew the facts and permit themselves to take "a bit of artistic license."

Toward the end of the text, *Life*, the authors write: "Today most biologists reject the biogenetic law, as Haeckel's view is called" (page 778). This sentence is at the far bottom of the left hand page as you look at the text. Your eye immediately scans up to the top of the next page (page 779) where the first thing you see is Figure 40.2 entitled: "Embryonic Resemblances." And what to your wondering eyes should immediately appear but a huge chart, seven inches wide by six inches high, of the embryo pictures almost identical to Haeckel's fraudulent drawings. **The authors of *Life* have made their disclaimer and covered their tracks, but the picture they leave with the student's mind is the same erroneous idea that Ernst Haeckel promoted in the 1880's!**

Christian parents, have you ever taken the time to look at the textbooks your Christian children are forced to study? You will be jolted to reality, if you do!

Beware lest any man spoil you through philosophy and vain deceit, after the tradition of men, after the rudiments of the world, and not after Christ (Colossians 2:8).

VESTIGIAL ORGANS

When this author was majoring in biology at Bucknell University back in the early 1960's, we were taught that the human body had more than 100 vestigial organs. (Actually the figure 180 was frequently tossed around.) These were supposedly useless organs and tissues left over from some evolutionary ancestors. Times have changed.

The only organ remaining that modern science has not found a current function for is the male nipple. Even this last vestige must now be deleted from the list with the advent of nipple piercing (a function?!).

In recent weeks I have skimmed six different biology textbooks looking for examples of "vestigial organs." They all had pictures very similar to Haeckel's with arrows pointing to what the textbooks call "gill slits." By calling the pharyngeal pouches "gill slits" or even "pharyngeal gill slits," a wrong idea is planted in the student's head. Gills are used for breathing. If evolution is true and humans evolved over millions of years from fishy ancestors, then it is only logical that humans should still retain some vestiges, in our embryonic days, of those epochs millions of years ago when we were fish. One of those vestiges of ages gone by is the formation of "gill slits" in the human embryo. Except for one thing—gill slits in the developing human in their mother's womb are never used for breathing underwater and actually have no relationship at all to fish gills.

The "gill slits" in humans are correctly called pharyngeal pouches. They form part of our middle ear, our parathyroid glands and our thymus gland. The evolutionists want to believe we humans came from fish so they label part of the developing human baby "gill slits," even though these pharyngeal pouches in humans have absolutely nothing to do with breathing under water while we are in our mother's womb or after we are born.

Tonsils are not vestigial. They are not left over from some ancient ancestor. They do have a function. Tonsils are part of our immune system, especially during our infancy. Third molars are quite functional in most people with some Caucasians being a common exception.

And another thing: these same textbooks have pictures of human embryos with part of the little baby labeled the "yolk sac." If we humans came from fish and reptiles, as the evolutionists teach, then we probably have something leftover from our reptile days when we came out of an egg. This is the organ that is labeled on the human embryos in the textbooks the "yolk sac." But this organ is in no way related to or resembles a fish or reptile egg. It has been mislabeled as a yolk sac to promote evolutionary images in the mind of the reader. This special organ made by the God of the Bible is the baby human's blood-forming organ and the textbooks should rightly call it what it is. It seems to me that we should use correct labels in our textbooks. But, let us never forget that we are in Satan's world system and it is built on deception. Satan is the father of lies!

We each have our own blood type, and it may not be the same as our mother's. When we are too tiny to have bones, but we still need blood to carry the nutrients throughout our little bodies, where does the blood come from? Our mother's blood does not go directly from her arteries into our arteries. As a matter of fact, we may have different types of blood altogether that would fight each other if they mixed together. So, God made the blood-forming organ to make each baby's special blood until the baby's bones develop enough maturity to take over the blood-making duties.

We know a family that the mother has Type O blood. When she was pregnant with her first child, whose blood was Type A, some of that baby's blood accidentally leaked into the mother's blood system. As a result, the mother built up antibodies in her blood against Type A blood. Then the mother got pregnant with the second baby. The second baby also had Type A blood. Some of the mother's blood leaked into the baby's circulatory system, and the mother's antibodies began killing the baby's blood cells. The doctor called this an ABO incompatibility reaction. That baby was very sick until it was cleansed of all of the mother's antibodies.

Vestigial organs are not vestigial. They have functions. Some organs can be surgically removed from humans (for example the appendix, which is part of our immune system when we are babies) because the Creator, the Lord Jesus, built backup systems into our miraculous bodies.

> ...thou hast covered me in my mother's womb. I will praise thee; for I am fearfully and wonderfully made: marvelous are thy works; and that my soul knoweth right well (Psalm 139:13b, 14).

NEANDERT(H)AL MAN

Orthodontist Jack Cuozzo, in his well-documented book, *Buried Alive* (Master Books, 1998), exposes the fraudulent depictions of the Neandertal skulls in the models and textbook pictures that our children must study. Dr. Cuozzo took cephalometric radiographic pictures of the Neandertal skulls and made a startling discovery. All the models and pictures of Neandertal skulls, that we have access to, have been altered.

When you go to the orthodontist, and he takes one of those x-rays of your head that allow him to make special measurements, it is a "cephalometric" radiograph. With this x-ray picture, he can precisely establish the way your teeth should come together (occlusion) in relationship to your jaw joint (temporomandibular joint). Dr. Cuozzo was able to precisely locate the position of Neandertal's teeth in relationship to his (or her) jaw joint with these radiographs.

His startling discovery was that in every picture and model we have, the lower jaw had been dislocated and thrust forward as much as an inch to give the erroneous impression that Neandertals had a lower face that stuck out (prognathism) like a monkey's lower jaw. When Dr. Cuozzo put the jaw back where it belonged, the Neandertals had a facial profile like modern man!

> **So God created man in his own image, in the image of God created he him; male and female created he them...And God saw everything that he had made, and, behold, it was very good. And the evening and morning were the sixth day (Genesis 1:27, 31).**

THE EVOLUTIONARY TREE OF LIFE

Those textbook pictures of the "tree" with a "simple" cell at the base and then lines going up into more and more complex plants and animals are a fraud. Take one of those pictures and erase the connecting trunk and branches. What you have left is a bunch of plants and animals scattered over a page that have no apparent familial relationship to each other at all. Some very creative evolutionists came up with these "tree of life" pictures to create the illusion that all living organisms are related to each other. These misleading textbook pictures have been successfully used to convince people that evolution is true and all living things are connected.

The reason they have the empty trunk and branches, with animals and plants only at the tips, is because the in-between forms (transitional forms) are nowhere to be found. These are called The Missing Links. The Missing Links are called missing links, first and foremost, because they are missing. They are not there! So the textbooks draw in the connecting lines to give us the illusion that the missing links are not really missing. This is textbook fraud! As the late Dr. Stephen Jay Gould wrote in *Natural History*, May 1977, p. 14:

> The extreme rarity of transitional forms [As far as this writer can tell, all Gould is saying with these big words is that the missing links are, in reality, actually missing. I think the missing links have been renamed "transitional forms" by the evolutionists because they do not appear to be as missing when the word "transitional" is utilized. But they are still missing. No one has found a direct link between fish and amphibian or cold-blooded reptile to warm-blooded mammal, etc.—Ed.] in the fossil record persists as the trade secret of paleontology. The evolutionary trees that adorn our textbooks have data only at the tips and nodes of their branches; the rest is inference, however reasonable, not the evidence of fossils.

So the textbook pictures of the "tree of life" show fully formed animals and plants, which are not evolving out of anything or into anything. In reality, they show exactly what the Bible teaches: God created each life-form after its own kind and there is nothing in between (except the imagination and inferences of the evolutionist).

> **And God said, "Let the earth bring forth grass, the herb yielding seed, and the fruit tree yielding fruit after his kind, whose seed is in itself, upon the earth: and it was so...."**
> **And God created great whales, and every living creature that moveth, which the waters brought forth abundantly, after their kind, and every winged fowl after his kind: and God saw it was good.... And God made the beasts after his kind, and cattle after their kind, and every thing that creepeth upon the earth after his kind: and God saw that it was good (Genesis 1:11, 21, 25).**

THE BUILDING BLOCKS OF LIFE

If you went to college in the fifties, you will remember the cheering professors when Stanley Miller and Harold Urey announced that they had formed the building blocks of life in their laboratory. Dr. Wells writes:

> There were problems, however. Scientists were never able to get beyond the simplest amino acids in their simulated primordial environment, and the creation of proteins began to seem not a small step, or a couple of steps, but a great, perhaps impassable divide.
>
> The telling blow to the Miller-Urey experiment, however, came in the 1970's, when scientists began to conclude that the Earth's early atmosphere was nothing like the mixture of gases used by Miller and Urey. Instead of being what scientists call a "reducing," or hydrogen rich environment, the Earth's early atmosphere probably consisted of gases released by volcanoes. Today there is near consensus among geochemists on this point. But put those volcanic gases in the Miller-Urey apparatus, and the experiment doesn't work—in other words, no "building blocks" of life.
>
> What do textbooks do with this inconvenient fact? By and large, they ignore it and continue to use the Miller-Urey experiment.... [But] they don't tell students that the researchers themselves now acknowledge that the explanation still eludes them.[159]

For the wrath of God is revealed from Heaven against all ungodliness and unrighteousness of men, who hold (hold back, suppress) the truth in unrighteousness.... Because that, when they knew God, they glorified him not as God, neither were thankful; but became vain in their imaginations, and their foolish heart was darkened. Professing themselves to be wise, they became fools (Romans 1:18, 21, 22).

SOME CONCLUDING COMMENTS TO THIS CHAPTER

Listed here are a few documented frauds foisted on our children in their textbooks and by their teachers who believe with unquestioning faith in the unsupported theory of macroevolution. Our children are being taught the religious

---

[159] Wells, "Survival of the Fakest," p.20.

worldview of Humanism (and Marxism) with its indispensable foundation—evolution. It is high time these perpetrators of fraud are held accountable! Why is this kind of blatant fraud winked at and tolerated by the esteemed ranks of academia?

The conflict between the ideas of creation and those of evolution are rooted in a major clash of worldviews. Our worldview is our basic set of beliefs. The values that we hold dear are a direct result of our worldview. Proverbs 23:7 tells us that **"...For as he thinketh in his heart, so is he."** What we believe about our existence will either spring up out of a biblical Christian worldview or out of one of the humanistic worldviews with their foundation of atheism and a billions-of-years-old universe.

Evolutionists and Creationists study exactly the same fossils. There is not a creationist set of fossils and an entirely different set of evolutionist fossils! The same holds true for the study of living animals. A creationist will not study animals that are any different from the animals examined by the evolutionist. We both study the same fossils, animals and universe. So, how can such widely different ideas (creation ideas versus evolution ideas) be gotten when educated people study the exact, same information? How can two Ph.D.'s graduate from the same university and one believes in a supernatural creation and the other believes in naturalistic evolution? The answer lies in their worldview. Both people have deeply religious convictions relating to their beliefs about origins. If there is no God, a person is forced to speculate about origins and how we might have gotten here through godless, naturalistic processes. Your worldview glasses determine your beliefs about origins.

OUR IDEAS DO HAVE CONSEQUENCES!

OUR WORLDVIEW ASSUMPTIONS
DETERMINE OUR CONCLUSIONS!

One set of beliefs gives the God of the Bible all the glory. The other belief systems give all the glory to man or to "Mother Nature." The fraud and deception of the evolutionary community robs our Heavenly Father of His glory and steals the praise reserved for Him alone (Isaiah 48:11)! These false worldviews lead us away from the simplicity and purity of devotion to Christ (2 Corinthians 11:3). Unfortunately, we are a people—even many in the church—who have been taken captive through philosophy and empty deception according to the tradition of men, and the elementary principles of the world, rather than according to Christ (Colossians 2:8).

The Creator, the Lord Jesus Christ, is the God of the impossible! Nothing is too difficult for him. He can speak the cosmos into existence, form man from dust and form woman from a rib (Jeremiah 32:17, 27).

It is the prayer of this author that every reader of this book will realize that they are living out their lives in a faith-based worldview. Either you have placed your faith in the idea of eternal matter, or your faith is resting in the eternal God of the Bible. Either idea has its consequences! Where have you placed your faith and trust concerning your eternal destiny? Never forget that eternity is a very long time compared to this little flick of time we spend on earth! But you can know for sure where you will spend eternity.

For the wages of sin is death; but the gift of God is eternal life through Jesus Christ our Lord...For whosoever shall call upon the name of the Lord shall be saved (Romans 6:23, 10:13).

MARVEL OF GOD'S CREATION

#10

The Woodpecker

If there is any animal that breaks the rules of evolution in such a way that it could not possibly have evolved, then it would need God as its Creator. The woodpecker is an example of such an animal. And if there is any animal (like the woodpecker) that must have needed God to create it, why not believe in God as the creator of everything else as well?

The woodpecker's beak is unlike that of other birds. It is designed to hammer its way into the hardest of trees. If the woodpecker evolved, how would it develop its thick, tough beak? Let's suppose some bird decided that there must be all kinds of little critters, which would be good for lunch, hidden beneath the bark of trees. This bird decided to peck through the bark and into the hardwood tree. On first peck, this bird discovered problems with the way it was put together. Its beak shattered when it slammed against the tree, its tail feathers broke, and it developed a migraine-strength headache.

With a shattered beak, the little bird was unable to eat and so it died. Now this bird began to think, "I must evolve a thicker beak and stronger tail feathers and something to help prevent headaches." Of course not! Dead animals cannot evolve anything. Yet the woodpecker not only has an industrial-strength beak, it also has a special cartilage between its head and beak to absorb some of the shock from the continuous drumming. Woodpeckers go home at night without a headache.

To help with the absorption of the constant pounding, the woodpecker has uniquely resilient tail feathers. It uses its tail feathers and feet to form a tripod effect as it clings to the tree. Even its feet are specially designed to enable it to move up, down, and around, vertical tree trunks. The feet of the woodpecker have two toes in front and two toes in back. Most other birds have three toes in front and one in back.

> This two-plus-two toe pattern...along with stiff yet elastic tail feathers, allows a woodpecker to grasp a tree firmly and balance itself on a vertical surface. When the woodpecker braces itself to chisel a hole, the tail feathers bend and spread, buttressing the bird against the rough tree surface. In this way feet and tail form an effective tripod to stabilize the blows of hammering into wood.[160]

Suppose that somehow a bird, knowing there was lunch in those trees, developed the strong beak, the shock absorber cartilage between the beak and the skull, the ability to move its head faster than you can tap fingers, the "two-plus-two" feet and the super stiff, yet, elastic tail feathers. This bird still has a major problem. It will starve to death. How could it drag its lunch out of the little insect tunnels in the tree? Have you ever attempted to drag an insect larva out of a tunnel? They hang on!

God has taken care of the woodpecker by creating in it a tongue that is several times longer than the average bird's tongue. Lester and Bohlin comment:

> ...the tongue of a woodpecker is in a class by itself. When chiseling into a tree, the woodpecker will occasionally come across insect tunnels. Its tongue is long and slender and is used to probe these tunnels for insects. The tip is like a spearhead with a number of barbs or hairs pointing rearward. This facilitates securing the insect while transporting it to the beak. A sticky

160 Lane P. Lester and Raymond G. Bohlin, *The Natural Limits to Biological Change* (Grand Rapids: Zondervan, 1984), p. 24.

glue-like substance coats the tongue to aid in this process as well.[161]

What a fascinating creation! Not only does the woodpecker have little barbs on the tip of its tongue, it is also a mini-glue factory. And the glue sticks securely to insects but does not stick to the beak of the woodpecker. Aren't God's creations marvelous!

But this is not all. Most birds have a tongue and a beak about the same length. The tongue of the woodpecker has evolutionists scratching their heads. It can be stretched far beyond the tip of the woodpecker's beak as it searches the larval tunnels for food. The animal kingdom displays no other tongues quite like that of the woodpecker. The tongue of some woodpeckers does not come from its throat up into its mouth like other creatures. For example, the European Green woodpecker's tongue goes down the throat, out the back of the neck "...around the back of the skull beneath the skin, and over the top between the eyes, terminating usually just below the eye socket."[162] In some woodpeckers the tongue exits the skull between the eyes and enters the beak through one of the nostrils! How would this evolve? And from what ancestor did the woodpecker inherit its special beak, feet, tail feathers, shock absorbing cartilage, thicker skull and unique tongue?

Did you know that a woodpecker opens and closes its eyes in between each peck? In between each rapid-fire peck the little bird opens its eyes, focuses, aims its beak, closes its eyes and then hits the tree with its pointed beak. Not only does the woodpecker close its eyes to keep the wood chips out, but also for another very important reason. Scientists have measured the force of the impact of the bird's head against the hardwood tree. The force is so powerful that if the bird did not close its eyes it would pop its eyeballs out! Have

[161] Ibid., p. 24.
[162] Ibid., p. 25.

you ever seen a blind woodpecker? They never forget to close their eyes. Only God could design this!

If evolution is true and if birds came from reptiles, many other changes would be necessitated. Many bones in woodpeckers (birds) are hollow to make them lighter for flight, but reptile bones are heavy. Birds do not have a bladder like reptiles do. This also helps to keep their weight down. They do not have to carry extra water-weight into their flight.

When woodpeckers and other birds sit on a branch their toes are attached to ligaments in such a way that the more they relax, the tighter their toes grasp the branch. This is the reason a strong wind can be blowing against a woodpecker sleeping on a branch and the bird does not blow off!

The woodpecker displays the glory of his Creator who is also our Creator. Why would an evolutionist study a marvel of God's creation such as the woodpecker and still refuse to believe in God the Creator? Only one answer seems to make sense! Pride! Pride! Pride!

Adrian Forsyth, evolutionist and expert on birds writes the following about a barn swallow (I'm sure it applies to woodpeckers as well):

> Darwin, however, freed the contemplative naturalist from that static point of view [that the God of the Bible created birds, Ed.]. As a consequence, every natural object offers our imaginations a history and biography. Rather than simply admiring the nest as a work woven without hands, we wonder how it came here and what its future is. More importantly, we begin to realize that barn swallows have not been passive pawns of omnipotent creation. They have had a role in their own fate.[163]

"Rational," humanistic man thinks that he himself is the "...master of his fate and the captain of his soul." This blinding pride does not allow the intrusion of a personal

---

[163] Adrian Forsyth, *The Nature of Birds* (Ontario, Canada: Camden house Publishing, 1988), p. 16.

sovereign Creator and God, but rather sees man as the pinnacle of all that is. The time has come for us to humble ourselves and bow before our infinitely righteous Almighty Creator!

> **If my people, which are called by my name, shall humble themselves, and pray, and seek my face, and turn from their wicked ways; then will I hear from heaven, and will forgive their sin, and will heal their land.**
>
> **Now mine eyes shall be open, and mine ears attent unto the prayer that is made in this place (2 Chronicles 7:14,15).**
>
> **Yea, all of you be subject one to another, and be clothed with humility: for God resisteth the proud, and giveth grace to the humble.**
>
> **Humble yourselves therefore under the mighty hand of God, that he may exalt you in due time:**
>
> **Casting all your care upon him; for he careth for you (1 Peter 5:5b-7).**
>
> **Let nothing be done through strife or vainglory; but in lowliness of mind let each esteem the other better than themselves.**
>
> **Look not every man on his own things, but every man also on the things of others.**
>
> **Let this mind be in you, which was also in Christ Jesus:**
>
> **Who, being in the form of God, thought it not robbery to be equal with God:**
>
> **But made himself of no reputation, and took upon him the form of a servant, and was made in the likeness of men:**
>
> **And being found in fashion as a man, he humbled himself, and became obedient unto death, even the death of the cross.**
>
> **Wherefore God also hath highly exalted him, and given him a name which is above every name:**
>
> **That at the name of Jesus every knee should bow, of things in heaven, and things in earth, and things under the earth;**
>
> **And that every tongue should confess that Jesus Christ is Lord, to the glory of God the Father** [Philippians 2:3-11, Emphasis added].

Prayer

"Have mercy upon me, O God, according to thy lovingkindness: according unto the multitude of thy tender mercies blot out my transgressions. Wash me thoroughly from mine iniquity, and cleanse me from my sin. For I acknowledge my transgressions: and my sin is ever before me. Against thee, thee only, have I sinned, and done this evil in thy sight: that thou mightest be justified when thou speakest, and be clear when thou judgest...Purge me with hyssop, and I shall be clean: wash me, and I shall be whiter than snow. Make me to hear joy and gladness; that the bones which thou has broken may rejoice. Hide thy face from my sins, and blot out all mine iniquities. Create in me a clean heart, O God..." (Psalm 51:1-4, 7-10a).

Blessed be the God and Father of our Lord Jesus Christ, who hath blessed me with all spiritual blessings in heavenly places in Christ: According as he hath chosen me in him before the foundation of the world, that I should be holy and without blame before him in love: Having predestinated me unto the adoption of children by Jesus Christ to himself, according to the good pleasure of his will, To the praise of the glory of his grace, wherein he hath made me accepted in the beloved. In whom I have redemption through his blood, the forgiveness of sins, according to the riches of his grace [Ephesians 1:3-7 (personal application paraphrase)].

Lord Jesus, I believe in You as my Lord and Savior. Help me to walk worthy of You unto all pleasing, being fruitful in every good work, and increasing in the knowledge of God (Adapted from Colossians 1:10).

CONCLUSION

You do not have to throw out your brains or any true, scientifically testable and verifiable science to believe in a literal six, 24-hour day creation that took place approximately six thousand years ago. We can believe that the Creator, the Lord and Savior Jesus Christ, created everything fully functional and mature. He displayed His ability to act without the human necessity of time by His miracles. Science that "proves" billions of years is based on many insupportable and unreasonable assumptions, fostered by the religion of Humanism, and fueled by the desire to be politically correct.

So we can believe the Bible as it addresses origins even though it does not tell us everything. If certain types of "science" contradict the Scriptures, we can be certain that these "sciences" are either mistaken or misinterpreted or misunderstood—because the Scriptures are eternal truth. The Bible is not exhaustive when it deals with science, but what it says is true! (See John 17:17; 8:32.)

Evolutionists admit to each other that "...the creationists have the better argument." This is because what we see in life and in the fossils does not display the emerging kinds of plants or animals that are so necessary to fulfill even the definition of macroevolution. Evolution from one cell to man is not scientifically observable at all. As my friend Mike Riddle likes to say, "Evolution has no explanation for life forms utilizing all left handed amino acids, no explanation for life starting with or without an oxygen atmosphere, no explanation for life starting in the ocean, and no explanation for the origin of information?"[164]

---

[164] See: Mark Riddle, *The Origin of Life Equipping Manual* (Training ETC, 6619 132nd Ave. NE, PMB 239, Kirkland, WA 98033-8627). E-mail: m.riddle@verizon.net

The universe is young—on the order of several thousand, not billions, of years old. Man, dinosaur and mastodon walked the earth at the same time. The missing links are missing! The transitional forms of life between the different kinds of plants and animals needed to prove evolution to be true have never been found! God created discrete plants and animals in The Beginning; with minor variations, these are what we see today. Mutations in the genes do not generate new life forms or even improve present life forms. Mutations harm or kill the organism into which they come. Prehistoric man was ape, monkey or man and not some genetically evolving apelike man or manlike ape.

The religious quest to prove evolution from the Big Bang to man will occupy the singular life of many, but will end in despair for all who pursue this myth of evolutionary faith.

Macroevolution is the attempt to answer the big questions: "How did I get here?" "Who am I?" and "Where am I going?" without belief in God. God Himself says:

The fool hath said in his heart, There is no God (Ps. 14:1).

Beware lest any man spoil you through philosophy and vain deceit, after the tradition of men, after the rudiments of the world, and not after Christ (Colossians 2:8).

Thus saith the Lord; Cursed be the man that trusteth in man, and maketh flesh his arm, and whose heart departeth from the Lord (Jeremiah 17:5).

O Lord, I know that the way of man is not in himself: it is not in man that walketh to direct his steps (Jeremiah 10:23).

There is a way which seemeth right unto a man, but the end thereof are the ways of death (Proverbs 14:12).

The conflict that started in Genesis 3 still rages today for the hearts and minds of people, yet the battle has already been won at the cross of Calvary.

> **For ye are bought with a price: therefore glorify God in your body, and in your spirit, which are God's (1 Corinthians 6:20).**

> **Forasmuch as ye know that ye were not redeemed with corruptible things, as silver and gold, from your vain conversation received by tradition from your fathers; But with the precious blood of Christ, as of a lamb without blemish and without spot (1 Peter 1:18,19).**

> **And having made peace through the blood of his cross, by him to reconcile all things unto himself; by him, I say, whether they be things in earth, or in heaven (Colossians 1:20).**

> **But God commendeth his love toward us, in that, while we were yet sinners, Christ died for us (Romans 5:8).**

> **That if thou shalt confess with thy mouth the Lord Jesus, and shalt believe in thine heart that God hath raised Him from the dead, thou shalt be saved (Romans 10:9).**

Psalm 1 tells us there are only two ways to walk in this world—on the path of the wicked, or the path of the righteous. God has revealed Himself in Creation and through the written Word as the "right way." We will all some day stand before Lord and King Jesus to answer for our lives lived in this world, and whether they have been lived for His eternal glory and praise, or for the praise of the power and glory of this world. Since the Fall of Genesis 3, man has been more interested in the approval of men, rather than the approval of God (John 5:44; 12:43). We compare ourselves with ourselves instead of with Christ and in so doing commit a great error (2 Corinthians 10:12)!

Even as "professing Christians," we have become a people who call **"evil good, and good evil"** (Isa. 5:20). More than anything else in these deceptive times in which we live, we have allowed ourselves to be **"corrupted from the simplicity that is in Christ"** (2 Cor. 11:3). We have not brought **"...into captivity every thought to the obedience of Christ"** (2 Cor. 10:5).

My challenge to Christian and non-Christian is to re-examine where our faith is actually invested. Is it possible that we have been seduced by the world's convincing "arguments of academia," impressive credentials and the ensuing "success, power, and prominence" that come from finding truth apart from God's Word? His Word is truth (John 17:17); it is eternal, living and active (Heb. 4:12), and will not return void (Isa. 55:11).

The non-verifiable "assumptions" of the scientific community are accepted without question in our hi-tech, sophisticated, humanistic, impersonal "politically correct" society...even by the majority of professing Christians who hide behind the hypocrisy of being "theistic evolutionists." (The theistic evolutionists say: "Yes, I'll acknowledge that there is a God, but He's not powerful enough to do anything other than to set the wheels in motion and let macroevolution take over!" Since any form of macroevolution is unbiblical, it is therefore sin to be a true Christian and hold to old universe evolutionary ideas. It is making God what we want Him to be. It is making God in our image. This is not much different than making a golden calf, is it?)

If professing Christians were in God's Word as much, or more than we are in the secular world's beliefs, then we would afford ourselves the opportunity to grow in the grace and knowledge of God's ways and to have the empowerment of the Holy Spirit to lead us into all understanding. 1 Cor. 3:18,19b states: **"Let no man deceive himself. If any man**

among you seemeth to be wise in this world, let him become a fool, that he may be wise. For the wisdom of this world is foolishness with God." Macroevolution is part of the wisdom of this world!

The bottom line always comes back to faith. Our ideas do have consequences! It is reported that Napoleon once said, "In the end the sword is always conquered by the mind." Are we going to believe by faith in eternal matter and energy, or eternal God? We all live by faith in one system or the other. No man can reason his way to saving faith in God because God is infinite and we are finite. He is the creator, and we are the created. He is holy, but we are sinful.

There is a great chasm caused by sin that separates the all-powerful God and Creator of the universe from His fallen creatures (us). When we refuse to accept our position under God in His creation (because of pride and rebellion), then we tend to look for comfortable alternatives. These alternatives allow us to escape from being created in the image of God and from being responsible to Him. They allow us to be independent from God, which will ultimately result in death and eternal separation from Him. Evolution is one of these alternatives!

Many times creationists are accused of trying to "discredit science" or scientists, an accusation which simply is not true. "Origins Science," as we know it, is based on many assumptions, which, by definition, cannot be proved. Assumptions become "truth" when the credentialed, powerful people of the world's system arrange data, and "logically" argue their case [see Chapter 10] while the "Christian" community stands by either accepting (they don't know what the Bible says), or defaulting, in that they don't have enough conviction to study the data and speak out for a creationist interpretation of factual science.

CHRIST DIED FOR PROUD SINNERS

The greatest truth that can ever be realized in this life is that Christ died for sinners.

For all have sinned and come short of the glory of God (Romans 3:23).

This is a faithful saying and worthy of all acceptation. For therefore we both labour and suffer reproach, because we trust in the living God, who is the Saviour of all men, specially of those that believe (1 Timothy 4:9,10).

The Lord is not slack concerning his promise, as some men count slackness; but is longsuffering to us-ward, not willing that any should perish, but that all should come to repentance (2 Peter 3:9).

But we see Jesus, who was made a little lower than the angels for the suffering of death, crowned with glory and honour; that he by the grace of God should taste death for every man (Hebrews 2:9).

For the grace of God that bringeth salvation hath appeared to all men, teaching us that, denying ungodliness and worldly lusts, we should live soberly, righteously, and godly, in this present world; looking for that blessed hope, and the glorious appearing of the great God and our Saviour Jesus Christ; Who gave himself for us, that he might redeem us from all iniquity, and purify unto himself a peculiar people, zealous of good works (Titus 2:11-14).

God gave His only begotten son to accomplish that act of love. Whether we are an unbelieving evolutionist, theistic evolutionist, or creationist is not the main issue. The issue is: "To whom will we bow for our eternal destiny?" Only pride and rebellion will keep us from enjoying that eternal rest in our Creator/Savior's complete forgiveness. We must realize that our salvation is provided by our Creator, Who is our Redeemer. It is not the Big Bang that will save us, but our

Creator-Redeemer, the Lord Jesus Christ, Who has spoken through time and space with His life and His Word, the Bible!

For God so loved the world, that he gave his only begotten Son, that whosoever believeth in him should not perish, but have everlasting life (John 3:16).

But the Lord is the true God, he is the living God, and an everlasting King: at His wrath the earth shall tremble, and the nations shall not be able to abide his indignation. He hath made the earth by his power, he hath established the world by his wisdom, and hath stretched out the heavens by his discretion (Jeremiah 10:10, 12).

I have made the earth, and created man upon it: I, even my hands, have stretched out the heavens, and all their host have I commanded (Isaiah 45:12).

Who knoweth not in all these that the hand of the Lord hath wrought this? In whose hand is the soul of every living thing, and the breath of all mankind (Job 12:9,10).

Come unto me, all ye that labour and are heavy laden, and I will give you rest. Take my yoke upon you, and learn of me; for I am meek and lowly in heart: and ye shall find rest unto your souls. For my yoke is easy, and my burden is light (Matthew 11:28-30).

Lo, I am with you alway, even unto the end of the world. Amen (Matthew 28:20b).

EPILOGUE

On February 12, 2002, when the revision of this book began in earnest, Dr. Sundarsingh Daniel arrived to help. We read the *Days of Praise* devotional together. This little devotional booklet comes from the Institute for Creation Research on a quarterly basis. It is excellent and readily available at www.ICR.org. The February 12th devotional seemed so appropriate that I am reproducing it for you as follows:

"How long, ye simple ones, will ye love simplicity? and the scorners delight in their scorning, and fools hate knowledge" (Proverbs 1:22)?

This ancient question by the wise man, Solomon, was posed almost 3000 years ago and is still relevant today. "How long?" he asked. How long will men continue to scoff at true knowledge? "The fear of the Lord is the beginning of knowledge: but fools despise wisdom and instruction" (Proverbs 1:7).

The answer to your question, Solomon, would have been 3000 years at least! Peter prophesied "that there shall come in the last days scoffers...saying, Where is the promise of His coming" (2 Peter 3:3,4)? And Paul said "that in the last days perilous times shall come. For men shall be...boasters, proud, blasphemers.... Ever learning, and never able to come to the knowledge of the truth" (2 Timothy 3:1,2,7).

Throughout history men have scorned the true knowledge of God and His Creation. Peter says they "willingly are ignorant," and Paul says they are "without excuse" (2 Peter 3:5; Romans 1:20), but they "delight in their scorning" nonetheless.

It is remarkable that their hatred of God's true knowledge is cloaked in a robe of scientism and evolutionary pseudo-knowledge that even deceives many professing Christians. "Professing themselves to be wise, they became fools" (Romans 1:22), despising the true wisdom and instruction of God's word.

"To the law and to the testimony: if they speak not according to this word, it is because there is no light in them" (Isaiah 8:20).

Those who scorn God's word have no light of their own, despite their scientific pretensions. "Wise men lay up knowledge: but the mouth of the foolish is near destruction" (Proverbs 10:14). HMM

Since Dr. Henry Morris got me started on this quest in 1971 with *The Genesis Flood*, I would like to leave you with this final thought in his words:

If there is anything certain in this world, it is that there is no evidence whatever that evolution is occurring today—that is, true vertical evolution, from some simpler kind to some more complex kind. No one has ever observed a star evolve from hydrogen, life evolve from chemicals, a higher species evolve from a lower species, a man from an ape, or anything else of this sort. Not only has no one ever observed true evolution in action, no one knows how evolution works, or even how it might work. Since no one has ever seen it happen (despite thousands of experiments that have tried to produce it), and no one yet has come up with a workable mechanism to explain it, it would seem that it has been falsified, at least as far as the present world is concerned. This does not prove it did not happen in the past, but the evolutionist should recognize that evolution is not science since it is not observable. Evolution must be accepted on faith [The Defender's Study Bible, Appendix 3].

Subject Index

Index of Authors

Scripture Index

Additional copies of
The Evolution of a Creationist
are available for $10.95 each.
(This includes postage and handling.)

BULK RATES ARE AVAILABLE

Please contact:

Biblical Discipleship Publishers
2212 Chisholm Trail
Rockwall, Texas 75032
(972) 771-0568
www.biblicaldiscipleship.org

Our thanks to Steve Greisen of Reel Productions
for donating the cover of this book
and for producing the videos,

Incredible Creatures that Defy Evolution Vols. I & II

Reel Productions can be contacted at
www.explorationfilms.com

Update 2008

God and His Word are **"the same yesterday, and today, and forever"** (Hebrews 13:8). They are unchanging. Since 1958 I have studied Biological Evolution, first as a convinced evolutionist but later (starting around 1971-1975) as a Bible-believing Christian creationist. Has much evolutionary "science" changed in those nearly fifty years? Yes, much of it! Has the Word of the Creator, the Lord Jesus Christ, changed? Not at all! So whose "word" do we believe deep down in our hearts—the changing words of men or the unchanging Word of God? Do I believe what the Bible says about origins history (although it is not exhaustive), or do I believe the big-bang-to-molecules-to-man origins story as presented by the atheistic, evolutionary community?

Many Christians do not appear to recognize or understand the importance of trusting the Creator and His teaching about the origin of all things as found in the early chapters of Genesis. We seem to think that as long as we believe in Jesus the meaning of those words in Genesis does not really matter. Then what we believe about origins--was it billions of years and a local flood, or thousands of years and a global flood--does not really matter either.

G. Richard Bozarth writes ("The Meaning of Evolution," *American Atheist*, Sept. 20, 1979, p. 30):

> Christianity has fought, still fights, and will fight science [Christianity does not fight true science; as a matter of historical record every major field in true science was founded by a Christian.] to the desperate end over evolution because evolution destroys utterly and finally the very reason Jesus' earthly life was supposedly made necessary. Destroy Adam and Eve and the original sin, and in the rubble you will find the sorry remains of the [S]on of [G]od. . . .If Jesus was not the [R]edeemer that died

for our sins, and this is what evolution means, then Christianity is nothing (Brackets mine).

Atheist Bozarth understands the importance of a literal Adam, Eve, and original sin better than many Christians. The argument is false that those early chapters of Genesis are poetry, allegory, and symbols and thus were never intended to be interpreted as literal history. The grammatical-syntactical form of Hebrew poetry is subject-verb-object: **"And God created great whales"** (Genesis 1:21). This is the way Genesis reads in English but not in Hebrew. The Hebrew is constructed with the form of verb-subject-object: **"Created God the great whales."** This is the correct form for Hebrew narrative. So Genesis is straight-forward Hebrew historical narrative. Genesis chapter one is intended to be understood as the true, narrative account of the history of God's six-day creation week. IT IS NOT POETRY; IT IS NARRATIVE! Therefore we should take it literally!

With the literal history of the creation week of our Creator, the Lord Jesus Christ (John 1, Colossians 1, Hebrews 1) taking place about 6000 years ago (see the genealogies), shouldn't there be some irrefutable evidence that our earth is thousands and not billions of years old?

Evidence for a Young Earth

Chapter 9 in this book lists some of the evidences for a young universe. In recent years creationist Ph.D. scientists with the *Institute for Creation Research* (www.icr.org), *Answers in Genesis* (www.answersingenesis.org), and the *Creation Research Society* (www.creationresearchsociety.org) have been involved in a project called, "Radioisotopes and the Age of the Earth" (RATE). They have found what many are considering to be irrefutable evidence that the earth is only a few thousand, not billions of years old.

One of the exciting discoveries the RATE scientists made is that there is Carbon-14 in coal and diamonds. Why is this significant evidence that the age of the earth can be measured in thousands and not billions of years?

> For some years there has been a growing realization that Carbon-14 atoms are found where they are not expected. With a half-life of 5,730 years, C-14 should no longer exist within "ancient" fossils, carbonate rocks, or coal. Yet small quantities of C-14 are indeed found in such samples on a worldwide scale. The RATE work extends this information with carbon-14 measurements in additional coal samples and also in diamonds. The RATE carbon-14 experiments on diamonds are the first ever reported in the literature. Measurable levels of carbon-14 are found in every case for both coal and diamond samples. This evidence supports a limited age for the earth.
> (Dr. Don DeYoung, *Thousands. . . Not Billions*, Green Forest: 2005, pp. 175, 176.)

Everyone must have assumed that coal and diamonds were millions of years old so, at least with diamonds, no one had ever bothered to check for C-14. If diamonds are really millions or even billions of years old there could be no C-14 remaining, hence, no reason to bother checking for C-14. But the RATE scientists decided to look, and found C-14 in all their sample diamonds! This appears to be irrefutable evidence that the diamonds were formed recently in an earth of only a few thousand years old. Young earth creationist scientists know from the Bible that the earth is only about 6000 years old. Therefore, it makes sense to look for short-lived C-14 in such things as diamonds even though evolutionary "science" would say "don't bother looking because diamonds are too old to retain any C-14."

There is one rather troubling item of information discovered by the RATE group. Apparently some researchers have found C-14 in coal in years gone by. Why has this information not been taught in the textbooks? Researchers have known for a while that coal cannot be 10 to 20 million years old because if it really was that old there would not be any measurable Carbon-14 remaining. We have not seen this scientific information on the front page of our newspapers or popular journals. Why not? The idea of C-14 in coal screams against the religious belief of evolution over billions of years establishing the age of the earth.

As Dr. DeYoung states, "The presence of C-14 in "very old" fossils, rocks, coal, and diamond samples is clearly in major conflict with the long-age time scale" (DeYoung, p. 56).

Another factor that relates to C-14 is the strength of earth's magnetic field. Earlier in this book (p. 238) the weakening of earth's magnetic field was discussed. Earth's magnetic field affects the amount of C-14 formed in our atmosphere. Earth's magnetism acts as a sort of filter or shield for certain types of cosmic radiation. The stronger earth's magnetic field is, the more of the necessary radiation is filtered out and less C-14 is formed. That would mean that to accurately date a bone using C-14, the strength of earth's magnetic field when the bone was in a living animal would have to be known to determine the amount of C-14 available in the atmosphere.

Let's say that an evolutionary scientist claims that a bone is 10,000 years old using C-14. Does anybody know how strong earth's magnetic field was 10,000 years ago? Certainly not! Well, then no one knows how much C-14 was available to be ingested by the animal that produced the bone. The meaning of this: C-14 can make *accurate* age determinations on organic material for just a few hundred years. Since the whole universe is only about 6000 years old, any date past that would be necessarily false. "The conclusion is that the pervasive presence of C-14 is strong evidence for a youthful earth" (DeYoung, p. 58). All things do not **"continue as they were from the beginning of the creation"** (2 Peter 3:4).

A Disagreement among Creationists

Thinking about all things continuing as they were from the beginning of the creation brings us to a point of difference between Christian creationists. Some who believe in young universe creation and a global flood in the days of Noah also believe that there was some sort of a water canopy surrounding our planet and above our atmosphere before the flood of Noah's day. This is discussed in chapter 9 of this book. Other Christian creationists do not believe that there was a water canopy surrounding earth before the Great Flood. In this sense these creationists believe all things continue as they were from the beginning of the creation. Psalm 148:3-6 is often quoted:

> **Praise ye him, sun and moon: praise him, all ye stars of light. Praise him, ye heavens of heavens, and ye waters that *be* above the heavens. Let them praise the name of the LORD: for he commanded, and they were created. He hath also stablished them for ever and ever: he hath made a decree which shall not pass.**

Psalm 148 seems to be saying that the Creator put some water in the heavens but out beyond the sun, moon and stars.

Two words in Genesis 1 may require some additional study on the part of the Hebrew scholars among whom this writer is not counted. What if "waters" (*mayim*) and "heavens" (*shamayim*) are, in truth, dual nouns? This is just a question! This is simply a speculation on my part. There are words in the Hebrew language that are called "dual nouns." These words usually refer to one thing that has two parts like a "pair" of trousers—one pair even though there are two distinct legs. An example in the Bible is the word translated "horns" in Psalm 22:21. There are two horns on the same animal. **Realizing that Hebrew commentators and lexicons (Brown-Driver-Briggs, Waltke and O'Connor, Gesenius, etc.) disagree with what I am about to say, I am going to**

say it anyway for the helpful debate that will hopefully develop! The following discussion is limited to the possible meaning of the two words mentioned above in Genesis chapter 1. If this argument has any merit there will then need to be further clarification of the use of these words in the Old Testament Scriptures.

The nouns for "waters" and "heavens" in Genesis chapter 1 are designated in the Hebrew as dual nouns, but the commentators do not think that they are actually meant to be translated in the dual sense. If this writer understands it correctly these nouns are thought of in a collective sense, not a dual sense. Here is the idea: Genesis 1:7 mentions the waters above the firmament and the waters under the firmament. The waters above and waters under are technically "dual." What if the "waters [dual] above" had two parts and the "waters [dual] under" also had been divided into two parts? The two parts of the waters above the firmament could then possibly be a water canopy around earth before the Flood as well as a second part of the water extending beyond the stars (Psalm 148:4). The dual meaning of the waters under the firmament could possibly be the waters on the surface of the earth and the waters under the surface of the earth. We plainly see the great bodies of water on the earth's surface, but there are also great bodies of water under the earth's surface. Almost anywhere on earth that wells are drilled sooner or later water is found. There are diverse life forms in both bodies of water.

It seems strange to me that our Lord would say "waters (dual) above" and then again "waters (dual) under" but not intend those words to be interpreted as dual nouns when a clear dualism is present in His creation which is what Genesis 1 is describing. And not only this, but he uses the dual form for heaven (*shamayim*) in the same passage. Could heaven also be one that is two? There is atmospheric heaven and stellar heaven. Atmospheric heaven is where the birds fly (Genesis 1:20). Stellar heaven is where the stars are (Genesis 1:14, 15).

There is also the Third Heaven which is where God lives. The Third Heaven is not part of our discussion.

If "waters" above, "waters" under, and "heavens" are intended to be interpreted as literal dual nouns it makes some of Genesis 1 and 2 easier to understand. If all the water was placed by God beyond the stars, it would not seem to have had any role in the rain that caused the Flood when the windows of Heaven were opened. This is why the creationists who believe God put all the water beyond the stars also believe that the water that came down as rain all originated in the "fountains of the deep" (Genesis 7:11). None of the Flood water came down from the waters above. Those waters were on the outside edge of outer space!

If one part of the divided waters was indeed a water canopy above stellar heaven, but the dual part was a water canopy surrounding earth above atmospheric heaven, the earth canopy could very well come down as rain and, combined with the water of the fountains of the deep, contribute to the rising Flood waters. This would also make the rainbow a NEW and special COVENANTAL sign after the Flood (according to those who believe that God put all the water out beyond the stars, Noah would have already seen many rainbows before the Flood since there was no water canopy surrounding earth and weather patterns would have been similar to today's weather from the very beginning. They thus believe that God would just have attached new meaning to the rainbow after the Flood). A water canopy around earth might help explain the long lifetimes of pre-Flood people, the huge size of fossil animals (fossil dragonflies with thirty two inch wing spans), evidence that planet earth was once pole-to-pole greenhouse warm, the fact that it did not rain on the earth and there is no record of falling rain until the Flood (Genesis 2:5, 6), Noah's one time drunkenness after the Flood (more rapid fermentation and cellular absorbtion rates after the collapse of the canopy due to less atmospheric pressure), etc.

One more possibility in the use of dual nouns is this: the dual is often used for geographical designations. For instance the dual noun form is used to refer to Jerusalem which is literally *Jerusalems* (some commentators call noun forms like this toponyms) but there is only one city. Here the dual is used in the geographical sense of the location of Jerusalem. If the dual form of Genesis 1 is used in this geographic sense with "waters" and "heavens" a bit more weight is added to the argument above. Of course our Lord may have used the dual form for Jerusalem to differentiate between the Jerusalem in Israel and the New Jerusalem of the future.

Other Hebrew nouns with dual endings but not translated in any dual sense are: Egypt (*Mitzrayim*) and noon (*tsacharayim*). Perhaps by using the dual form of Egypt and noon the writer of Genesis had a dual meaning in mind even though the commentators do not think so. Moses lived in Egypt one third of his life. He knew Egypt. Egypt was divided into two parts—north Egypt and south Egypt. Noon was and is the division point in any day. The day is in two parts, A.M. and P.M, morning and evening or morning and afternoon.

To sum it all up—waters and heavens of Genesis 1 are technically dual nouns. If interpreted as duals, which no one seems to do, "waters above" would be divided into two bodies. The water above stellar "heaven," and water above atmospheric "heaven." The "waters under," also divided into two bodies, would be the water on the surface of the earth and the water under the surface of the earth. With this interpretation the dual nouns could be interpreted as actual duals and certain problems listed above would disappear as well as certain differences between fellow Christian creationists.

For those well-studied in the idea of a pre-flood water canopy, it is my understanding that there is a heat problem no matter what model of origins is preferred. All origin's models are built upon faith. No one was there and no true science can duplicate or reproduce The Beginning. The only record of the beginning of everything that we have is the written Word of our Lord Jesus. All of us struggle with the interpretation of God's Word.

> **God *is* our refuge and strength, a very present help in trouble. Therefore will not we fear, though the earth be removed, and though the mountains be carried into the midst of the sea; *Though* the waters thereof roar *and* be troubled, *though* the mountains shake with the swelling thereof. Selah (Psalm 46:1-3).**

The Probability of the Universe and Life Happening by Mindless Chance

Another problem for the religious faith belief in evolution (which says that life forms exist as a result of mindless, non-directed, non-purposeful, random, chance, accidental processes over millions of years with no God) is the probability of it happening at all. In 1860, Thomas Huxley proposed that "given enough time and material, six monkeys could type the 23rd Psalm simply by randomly punching the keys" (as referenced in *Evolution Exposed* by Roger Patterson, Hebron, KY: Answers In Genesis: 2006, p. 144. This book exposes the scientifically untrue material in major public schools' science textbooks).

Patterson goes on to say,

> Assuming a 50-key typewriter to accommodate letters, numbers, and punctuation, the chance of typing "THE" is one in 50x50x50... or one in 125,000. At a rate of one strike per second this would take 32.75 hours. For the phrase "THE LORD" the chance becomes 50 [to the minus 8th power] and requires 1,238,663.7 years. The entire Psalm requires 9.552 [times 10 to the 1016th power] years to complete on average (Patterson, p. 144).

Think about this for a minute. We would have six extraordinarily old monkeys still typing away at the Twenty-third Psalm on into eternity!

Many evolutionists claim that the universe is around 15 billion years old (7.3 to 20 billion is in the literature). There is not enough time starting at the evolutionary "beginning" for the six monkeys to show any progress in their Psalm's project right up to until now! But does 15 billion years give adequate time for chemicals to evolve and then go on to mindlessly morph into DNA and, yes, life itself?

Patterson continues,

> When considering the probability of the assembly of a DNA molecule, the same problems arise. Harold J. Morowitz, professor of biophysics at Yale, has calculated that the formation of one *E. coli* bacteria in the universe at . . .one in 10 to the power of 100 billion. Sir Fred Hoyle [evolutionist and proposer of the Steady State hypothesis] has offered the analogy of a tornado passing through a junkyard and assembling a Boeing 747, "nonsense of a high order" in his words. Natural selection cannot be the mechanism that caused life to form from matter as it can only work on a complete living organism.... Another major problem with the probability argument is that the chemical processes that supposedly formed life are reversible at every step. As water is released in the formation of amino acids, the water is available to break the bond in the reverse reaction, which is actually more favorable. Oceans are the last place amino acids would form. Huxley's typewriters would have to include a delete key for each other key in order for the analogy to be complete. No matter how much time and matter was available or the rate of interaction of atoms, the probability remains zero for the reversible reactions involved. The many distinct interactions within living systems clearly point to the presence of a designer, the God of the Bible (p. 145).

There is a way that seemeth right unto a man, but the end thereof are the ways of death (Proverbs 14:12).

Natural Selection Proves Evolution?

Does Natural Selection prove the evolution of reptiles to dogs? First, Natural Selection can only function within the limited genetic information that is already present in the population of animals or plants. Let us not forget that *information is non-material*. There is no way to capture or grab hold of a piece of information to insert it into a gene, nor is there a known procedure to remove information from a gene. The gene and the information that it contains are a single unit. Therefore any and all genetic information had to have been inserted into all genomes, both animal and plant, by some supernatural power at the time of their origin. **"Did not he that made me in the womb make him? And did not one fashion us in the womb?"** (Job 31:15) **"Thine eyes did see my substance, yet being unperfect; and in thy book all *my members* were written, *which* in continuance were fashioned, when *as yet there was* none of them"** (Psalm 139:16). Yes, genes can mutate, recombine, turn on, turn off, drop out, and display an advantage or disadvantage to a life form, but no NEW information can ever be added to a genome. New and different expressions of the genes as they change (information drops out) or recombine, of course, but no insertion of NEW genetic information means no true evolution of one kind of animal or plant into some other kind of life form. Bacteria remain bacteria!

In an article in *Scientific American*, "The Fossil Fallacy" March 2005, p. 32, by Michael Shermer, creationists are rebuked, according to Shermer, for not understanding evolution. Shermer, a good writer by the way, uses the evolution of the dog (natural selection) as his example of evolution in action. He states that all dogs evolved from a common Eurasian wolf pair many years ago. The geneticists claim to have proven this. If the geneticists are correct, this poses no problem for the creationist. We would say that the God of the Bible brought a common Eurasian wolf pair to Noah and the ark before He judged sin with the global flood.

Shermer uses dog "evolution" (as his example to the creationists that he believes do not understand evolution) to prove that evolution is true. There is a problem here. To go from a Eurasian wolf pair to Fifi the Poodle over hundreds of years proves just the opposite of evolution. To have true evolution occur NEW information would have to be added to the Eurasian wolf pair genes all along the way. We know that information cannot be added to any gene since it is non-material and cannot be captured. Thus, to get from the Eurasian wolf to Fifi, information must have been lost, not NEW information gained. How do we know this? It is impossible to breed a Poodle backwards into an Eurasian wolf. The information is no longer there! Shermer's example supports the creation of the dog-kind at a point of time in the past with all the genetic information in place. Then, over the years, genetic information has gotten lost and the Poodle, no matter how elegant its hairdo, is, genetically, a weaker dog which requires much more care than a Eurasian wolf.

Biology: The Living Science, a Biology textbook states, "[A]n important point to remember is that the variety of genes carried by all living species is the result of millions of years of random mutation, natural selection, and genetic drift" (Miller, K. and J. Levine, Englewood Cliffs, NJ: Prentice Hall, 1998, p. 271). This is a typical evolutionary statement, but where does all the information come from? Millions of years, random mutation, natural selection and genetic drift do not produce one iota of BRAND NEW genetic information. Perhaps a different or even new characteristic is produced by changes in or recombinations of the genes but no NEW genetic information has been magically added to the total gene pool. This means that the original bacteria are still bacteria because bacteria information is all the information that they were given by our Creator! Bacteria have never evolved and never will evolve into fish. It is impossible for molecules to generate life and then, over millions of years of additions of NEW genetic information, produce mankind. However, this IS the argument [millions of years] that evolutionists will always use as their battle cry to prove that evolution has occurred, which goes against all true scientific evidence and the true historical evidence of the Bible.

Are Dinosaur Fossils Millions of Years Old?

The most popular creatures that the evolutionary community uses for teaching evolution in combination with millions of years are dinosaurs. Children are introduced to the "terrible lizards" in TV shows, movies, cartoons, and classrooms from the earliest days of their government schooling. Since the children do not see any dinosaurs in their backyard or on their way to school, it is easy to convince them that the big reptiles went extinct as much as 65 million years ago. However, a huge surprise was in store for the old earth evolutionists. Montana State University's Dr. Mary Schweitzer discovered elastic soft tissue, blood vessels, and even red blood cells in the excavated bones of a giant T. rex! This cannot be if the T. rex is 65 million years old. Of course it is easy to understand if the giant reptile was buried in a global flood a few thousand years ago. The evolutionists are now trying to prove a mechanism that would preserve elastic soft tissue and red blood cells for 65 million years in a buried dinosaur bone. They will not just admit that this T. rex can only be a few thousand years old. (For more information see: www.answersingenesis.org, go to "get archives" then to "article archives" then to "Dinosaur soft tissue find—a stunning rebuttal of 'millions of years,'" by Dr. Carl Wieland.)

Where is the testable, reproducible, experimentally verifiable evidence that big bang to molecules to life to man evolution is true? As each area of true science (in contrast to the false "science" of evolution based on millions of years) is more fully investigated it becomes glaringly evident: the preponderance of evidence supports the origin and creation of everything a few thousand years ago as reported in the Bible. Genesis is straight-forward Hebrew historical narrative. It is not just symbols and poetry. The discovery of C-14 in coal and diamonds strongly supports the Genesis teaching of an earth a few thousand (not billions) of years old. Soft tissue in excavated dinosaur bones supports the Biblical account. The laws of probability show that there is no way that the evolutionist's Big Bang could mindlessly produce organic, thinking people from lifeless, inorganic matter in *any* amount of time.

It appears that, when verifiable, truly scientific evidence is examined, the creationists still have the best arguments! We can trust the Word of our God, the Bible, from page one.

There is a massive deception in our day. Satan is a liar and the father of lies (John 8:44) and people would rather believe a lie than the truth. The prophet Isaiah said it this way:

> **Because ye have said, We have made a covenant with death, and with hell are we at agreement; when the overflowing scourge shall pass through, it shall not come unto us: for we have made lies our refuge, and under falsehood have we hid ourselves** (Isaiah 28:15).

The Lord Jesus made a similar statement in John chapter 8:

> **Ye are of *your* father the devil, and the lusts of your father ye will do. He was a murderer from the beginning, and abode not in the truth, because there is no truth in him. When he speaketh a lie, he speaketh of his own: for he is a liar, and the father of it. And because I tell *you* the truth, ye believe me not.**
>
> **Which of you convinceth me of sin? And if I say the truth, why do ye not believe me? He that is of God heareth God's words: ye therefore hear *them* not, because ye are not of God** (John 8:44-47).

Intelligent Design and Progressive Creation

Since I last revised this book, the Progressive Creationists (Hugh Ross, Fuz Rana, Reasons to Believe Ministries, etc.) have grown in their acceptance and popularity as have the Intelligent Design people (Philip Johnson, Michael Denton, Jonathan Wells, Michael Behe, Discovery Institute, etc.). Many of the Design scientists are Christian Theistic evolutionists, some are Theistic evolutionists, and a few are Atheistic evolutionists who see design in their area of research and study. The major speakers and writers that I have met personally (both Progressive Creationists and Intelligent Design scientists) are "old earth, local flood" [The earth is billions of years old and the Flood of Noah's Day was a local river overflow confined to the Mesopotamian valley]. This contrasts with the Biblical account that records a young earth (see the genealogies) and a global flood (see Genesis 6-8) in the days of Noah.

On the university campuses, the Design speakers use their expertise in true science to back the evolutionists into an intellectual corner. They do not, however, show the intellectuals The Way (Jesus) out of the corner, but without exception they do a great job of using true science to prove that everything in this universe is convincingly designed. The major Design speakers will not take a position on the Bible, nor will they say who the Designer is when they are in campus environments. Perhaps this is okay for a secular university campus, but in my opinion, this (having Intelligent Design speakers) is not appropriate for the church. When "old earth local-flood" Progressive Creationists and Intelligent Design speakers are given the pulpit in a church, they thoroughly confuse some of our Christian brothers and sisters. People who originally believed in the young earth, global flood as recorded in the Bible are often stripped of their trust in the early chapters of Genesis by these very intelligent teachers. This is heresy penetrating the church! It is weakening the faith of the precious believers for whom our Lord Jesus shed His blood.

> But take heed lest by any means this liberty of yours become a stumblingblock to them that are weak. For if any man see thee which hast knowledge sit at meat in the idol's temple, shall not the conscience of him which is weak be emboldened to eat those things which are offered to idols; And through thy knowledge shall the weak brother perish, for whom Christ

died? But when ye sin so against the brethren, and wound their weak conscience, ye sin against Christ (1Corinthians 8:9-12).

The God of the Bible, the Creator and Redeemer of all, the Lord Jesus Christ says,

I am the bread of life: he that cometh to me shall never hunger; and he that believeth on me shall never thirst. But I said unto you, that ye also have seen me, and believe not. All that the Father giveth me shall come to me; and him that cometh to me I will in no wise cast out. For I came down from heaven, not to do mine own will, but the will of him that sent me. And this is the Father's will which hath sent me, that of all which he hath given me I should lose nothing, but should raise it up again at the last day. And this is the will of him that sent me, that every one which seeth the Son, and believeth on him, may have everlasting life: and I will raise him up at the last day (John 6:32-40).

Global Warming: Does Earth Really Have a Fever?

TIME, APRIL 3, 2006, p. 28-45

"The image of Earth as organism—famously dubbed Gaia by environmentalist James Lovelock—has probably been overworked, but that's not to say the planet can't behave like a living thing, and these days, it's a living thing fighting a fever."

"Earth has a fever!"
Al Gore to the United States Senate, March 21, 2007

Global warming is a political strategy of Marxists, Socialists, and liberal politicians.
Strategy:
Create a life-threatening global crisis (we are causing earth to overheat and we will die).

Advertise the crisis repeatedly (Gore and his propaganda movie in government schools).

Gain a critical mass of people (using media and Marxist/ Socialist mislead celebrities).

Pass laws that restrict industry, private property and freedom (No oil drilling).

Decrease local citizen's control and increase central government's control and taxes.

Confiscate private property (your factory is dirty; you are destroying wetlands).

Abolish the free-market economic system (government control of education, medicine, sports, business, music, internet, farming, our house themostats, etc. and all of this is to "save our lives").

The ultimate goal: Establish a two class civilization:
  • The Elites
  • And everyone else (slaves with no rights?)

But the day of the Lord will come as a thief in the night; in the which the heavens shall pass away with a great noise, and the elements shall melt with fervent heat, the earth also and the works that are therein shall be burned up (2 Peter 3:10).

"You wouldn't know it from Al Gore's *An Inconvenient Truth,* but there are many upsides to global warming: . . ." says Dr. Fred Singer, Professor Emeritus of Environmental Studies, University of Virginia. In addition Dr. Fred Singer also holds the following accomplishments: Distinguished Research Professor at George Mason University, president of the Science and Environmental Policy Project; Ph.D. in Physics from Princeton University; founding dean of the School of Environmental and Planetary Sciences at University of Miami; founding director of the U.S. National Weather Satellite Service; past vice-chairman of the U.S. National Advisory Committee on Oceans and Atmosphere.

Dr. Fred Singer is one of the most qualified environmental scientists in the world, and he is not at all concerned with the present liberal and celebrity faddishness that we are about to be destroyed by <u>human-generated</u> global warming.

Dr. Singer says:

> In the past few years there has been increasing concern about global climate change on the part of the media, politicians, and the public. It has been stimulated by the idea that human activities may influence global climate adversely and that therefore corrective action is required on the part of governments. Recent evidence suggests that this concern is misplaced. Human activities are not influencing the global climate in perceptible ways. Climate will continue to change, as it always has in the past, warming and cooling on different time scales and for different reasons, regardless of human action. I would also argue that—should it occur—a modest warming would be on the whole beneficial. This is not to say that we don't face a serious problem. But the problem is political. [<u>Is Al Gore a lifetime politician or a Ph.D. in Environmental Science?</u>] Because of the mistaken idea that governments can and must do something about climate, pressures are building that have the potential of distorting energy policies in a way that will severely damage national economies, decrease standards of living, and increase poverty. This misdirection of resources will adversely affect human health and welfare in industrialized nations, and even more in developing nations. Thus it could well lead to increased social tensions within nations and conflict between them.
>
> If not for this economic and political damage, one might consider the present concern about climate change nothing more than just another environmentalist fad, like the Alar apple scare or the global cooling fears of the 1970s. Given that so much is at stake, however, it is essential that people better understand the issue....But in seeking to understand recent warming, we also have to consider the natural factors that have regularly warmed the climate prior to the industrial revolution and, indeed, prior to any human presence on the earth. After all, the geological record shows a persistent 1,500 year cycle of warming and cooling extending back at least one million years. [The 1500 year cycles are evident—but only for about 4500 years, not

millions, depending on your worldview.] (www.hillsdale.edu/news/imprimis.asp, Dr. Fred Singer, "Global Warming: Man-Made or Natural," *Imprimis,* 36, no. 8, (August 2007): 1f.

Please go to the Hillsdale college web page and read Dr. Singer's entire article.

"The continued <u>rapid cooling</u> of the earth since WWII is in accord with the increase in global air pollution associated with industrialization, mechanization, urbanization and exploding population" (Reid Bryson, "Global Ecology; Readings Toward a Rational Strategy for Man," 1971).

So in 1971 the scientists were saying that human-generated global air pollution associated with industrialization, mechanization, urbanization, and exploding population was instrumental in *GLOBAL COOLING*! But, Al Gore and the Kyoto crowd say that these are the essential causative factors in global warming.

"The threat of a new ice age must now stand alongside nuclear war as a likely source of wholesale death and misery for mankind" (Nigel Calder, *International Wildlife*, June, 1975).

> From 1880 to about 1940 the world—particularly the Northern Hemisphere—went through a period of significant warming . . . .but since about 1940, there has been a distinct drop in average global temperature. It's fallen about ½ a degree Fahrenheit—even more in high latitudes of the Northern Hemisphere (Dr. J. Murray Mitchell, Jr., National Oceanic and Atmospheric Administration, "What's happening to our climate?" *National Geographic* November 1976, p. 581).

"During the last 20 to 30 years, world temperature has fallen, irregularly at first but more sharply over the last decade" (U.S. National Science Board, 1974, as quoted in *National Geographic,* Nov. 1976, p. 581).

> England's annual growing season shrank by 9 or10 days between 1950 and 1966," Hubert Lamb has noted (Britain's University of

East Anglia). "In the northern tier of the U.S. Midwest, summer frosts again occasionally damage crops. Sea ice has again returned to Iceland's coast after more than 40 years of virtual absence. Glaciers in Alaska and Scandinavia have slowed their recession; some in Switzerland have begun advancing again. Earth's spinning motion steers. . . an ever-changing weather system (*National Geographic*, Nov. 1976, p. 581).

NATIONAL ACADEMY OF SCIENCES, 1975: "The climates of the earth have always been changing, and they will doubtless continue to do so in the future. How large these future changes will be, and where and how rapidly they will occur we do not know."

All the more reason that we should follow the admonition of I Pet. 4:19: **"Wherefore let them that suffer according to the will of God commit the keeping of their souls *to him* in well doing, as unto a faithful Creator."**

Of course most of these quotes are from the 1970's and Al Gore and the global warming, politically correct crowd have made massive progress in forecasting "indisputable", "factual", "scientifically verifiable" evidence that our earth is going to overheat to the extinction of life in the next few decades (without sufficient scientific facts to verify their claims). As recently as 1992 scientists were predicting a "guaranteed" global cooling leading to a devastating ice age.

"The advent of a new ice age, scientists say, appears to be guaranteed. The devastation will be astonishing" (Greg Easterbrook, "Return of the Glaciers," *Newsweek*, November 23, 1992).

Are any scientists today disagreeing with the human generated global warming propaganda of the Al Gore political crowd and the liberal media? Dr. Fred Singer and his Hillsdale college speech were mentioned already, and here (notice the date) is another well qualified environmental scientist:

Wednesday, June 20, 2007, *Ottawa Financial Post*: "The mud at the bottom of B.C. fjords reveals that solar output drives climate change—and that we should prepare now for dangerous global cooling" (Dr. Timothy Patterson, professor and director of the Ottawa-Carleton Geoscience Centre, Department of Earth Sciences, Carleton University, Ottawa, Canada, p.3).

Dr. Patterson continues:

In some fields the science is indeed "settled." For example, plate tectonics, once highly controversial, is now so well-established that we rarely see papers on the subject at all. But the science of global climate change is still in its infancy, with many thousands of papers published every year.   In a 2003 poll conducted by German environmental researchers Dennis Bray and Hans von Storch, two-thirds of more than 530 climate scientists from 27 countries surveyed did not believe that "the current state of scientific knowledge is developed well enough to allow for a reasonable assessment of the effects of greenhouse gases." About half of those polled stated that the science of climate change was not sufficiently settled to pass the issue over to policymakers at all....Solar scientists predict that, by 2020, the sun will be starting into its weakest Schwabe solar cycle of the past two centuries, likely leading to unusually cool conditions on Earth.

Beginning to plan for adaptation to such a cool period, one which may continue well beyond one 11-year cycle, as did the Little Ice Age, should be a priority for governments. It is global cooling, not warming, that is the major climate threat to the world, especially Canada. As a country at the northern limit to agriculture in the world, it would take very little cooling to destroy much of our food crops, while a warming would only require that we adopt farming techniques practiced to the south of us.

Dr. R. Timothy Patterson concludes:

"Meantime, we need to continue research into this, the most complex field of science ever tackled, and immediately halt wasted expenditures on the King Canute-like task of 'stopping climate change.'" [Dr. Tim Patterson is Professor of Geology at Carleton University in Ottawa, Ontario, Canada. He received both a B.Sc. in Biology (1980) and a B.A. in Geology (1983) from Dalhousie University, Halifax, N.S. and a Ph.D. in Geology from the University of California at Los Angeles (UCLA) in

1986. After brief stints at the University of Southern California and University of California at Berkeley he joined Carleton University in 1988 as an Assistant Professor. He was promoted to Full Professor in 1999. He is Canadian leader of the International Geological Correlation Program Project IGCP 495 "Quaternary Land-Ocean interactions" and is Principal Investigator of a Canadian Foundation for Climate and Atmospheric Sciences project studying high-resolution Holocene climate records from anoxic fjords and coast lakes in British Columbia.]

The Age, April 7, 2003
"Research Casts Doubt on Global Warming"

"Claims that man-made pollution has caused unprecedented warming have been undermined by research that shows the earth was warmer in the Middle Ages (800-1300 A.D.). The review by a Harvard University team . . .proves that the world had a medieval warm period between the 9th and 14th centuries with world temperatures significantly higher than today."

The hottest temperatures recorded in the U.S.A. were in the 1930's peaking in 1934. These temperatures were hotter than the "global warming mantra" that 1998 and following have been the hottest on record.

It appears that Al Gore and his environmentalist friends have told us only one side of the global warming versus global cooling story!

Another web page that interviews the world's leading environmental scientists is www.greatglobalwarmingswindle. com.

The Lord Jesus has it all under control. Certain things must happen in the last days of this age, one of which is massive deception. As the Lord says in Matthew 24:24: **For there shall arise false Christs, and false prophets, and shall show great signs and wonders; insomuch that, if it were possible, they shall deceive the very elect.**

Why are large numbers of clergy, seminary professors, university professors, Christian school teachers and politicians supporting the global warming crowd? It seems to boil down to money (grants) and academic pride (being "politically correct" which is loving the honor and approval and praises of men, more than the praise of God, John 5:44 and 12:43).

Beware lest any man spoil you through philosophy and vain deceit, after the tradition of men, after the rudiments of the world, and not after Christ (Colossians 2:8).

If we call ourselves Christians we should be impeccable stewards of planet earth and its resources for the glory of the Creator, our Savior, the Lord Jesus Christ.

So let us be alert, keeping our hearts and minds fixed on the Lord Jesus through His Word, the Bible. Let us not be led astray by the false philosophies and theories of men.

But I fear, lest by any means, as the serpent beguiled Eve through his subtilty, so your minds should be corrupted from the simplicity that is in Christ (2 Corinthians 11:3).

But the LORD *is* **the true God, he** *is* **the living God, and an everlasting king: at his wrath the earth shall tremble, and the nations shall not be able to abide his indignation. Thus shall ye say unto them, The gods that have not made the heavens and the earth,** *even* **they shall perish from the earth, and from under these heaven. He hath made the earth by his power, he hath established the world by his wisdom, and hath stretched out the heavens by his discretion. When he uttereth his voice,** *there is* **a multitude of waters in the heavens, and he causeth the vapours to ascend from the ends of the earth; he maketh lightnings with rain, and bringeth forth the wind out of his treasures** (Jeremiah 10:10-13).

What does the Creator of everything, the Lord Jesus Christ, say?

Thus saith the LORD, thy redeemer, and he that formed thee from the womb, I *am* **the LORD that maketh all** *things***; that**

stretcheth forth the heavens alone; that spreadeth abroad the earth by myself (Isaiah 44:24).

While the earth remaineth, seedtime and harvest, and cold and heat, and summer and winter, and day and night shall not cease (Genesis 8:22).

The Incredible Brazil Nut Tree

The Brazil nut tree is a prominent resident of the Amazon jungle. This tree grows to a height of 180 to 200 feet and is one of the major support trees of the Amazon rainforest canopy. It is a testimony to its Creator, the Lord Jesus.

The Brazil nuts are actually not nuts at all. A true nut is designed with two halves, such as peanuts, pecans, walnuts, and cashews. A seed is a single unit, not two halves. The Brazil nut should be called the Brazil seed since it does not have two halves. The nuts (seeds) form in a pod about the size of a large coconut. The pod is rock hard and can weigh up to five pounds.

The native people of the Amazon rainforest know which trees bear nuts so they build their trails out around them. It is somewhat uncomfortably lethal to be struck on the head with a five pound pod dropping from 180 feet in the air! The pods are so tough they do not even split open when they hit the ground. Of course if the pods are not opened the nuts (seeds) cannot get out and no new Brazil nut trees would start to grow.

In the Amazon rainforest there is a small rodent called an *Agouti*. This is the animal that our Creator designed and made to open the pods and pull out the nuts. The *Agouti* likes to eat Brazil nuts and has the knowledge and equipment to do just that. When it finds a pod it chews into it and makes a hole large enough to get the nuts out. It has been said that an incredible characteristic of the *Agouti* is that each one chews its own signature hole into the pod. The hole is like our finger print. Some holes are round, some oval, some star-shaped, some almost square, some large, some small. How can this be? How would evolution explain this? But there is more.

When the little rodent pulls out the nuts it eats some and buries some thinking it will retrieve the buried ones later. A few nuts are forgotten and sprout and grow into mature trees. These mature trees bloom with special flowers. The flower has its pollen in a sealed spiral tube. Only one insect has the knowledge and necessary equipment to get at the pollen. That insect is the *Brazil Nut Long-tongued bee*. This special bee has strong jaws and a very long tongue. With its strong jaws it holds open the closed end of the flower and inserts its long tongue down the spiral tube to the pollen. As it goes from flower to flower it pollinates the Brazil nut tree.

So in the jungle in order to have Brazil nuts there must be the mature tree, the *Agouti* and the *Brazil Nut Long-tongued bee*. But that is not all. For the bees to reproduce, a particular species of orchid must be present. Before Mrs. Bee will invite Mr. Bee into her house so that there can be baby bees, he must find the special orchid and get the scent of that one species of orchid on himself. Only then will Mrs. Bee play hostess to Mr. Bee!

What then is required to have Brazil nut trees growing and reproducing in the Amazon rainforest? There must be the tree, the *Agouti*, the *Brazil Nut Long-tongued bee* and the particular species of orchid! If any one of these is missing there will be no Brazil nut.

How would this complex system with all its required parts come into existence through the mindless, non-directed, non-purposeful, accidental, chance processes of godless evolution over millions of years? All four required elements must be mature and fully functional from their beginning. All are needed and all at the same time and in the same place with the necessary information and specialized equipment! Only the Creator, the Lord Jesus, could engineer such a wonderfully designed biological system.

How does the *Agouti* know that there is a tasty treat inside the pod? If he did know, but did not have the necessary teeth and jaw structure, he would not be capable of getting the seeds out of the pod.

Did the *Brazil Nut Long-tongued bee* just happen to come along at the right time and in the right place to pollinate the tree? Of course it had to have the strong jaw and long tongue to get the pollen, but how does it know the pollen is in the spiral tube?

Does the orchid somehow know that it needs to grow near the Brazil nut tree so that it will be available for the male *Brazil Nut Long-tongued bee* to get the orchid's scent on himself so that the female bee will not reject his courtship? And as he acquires the scent of the orchid he pollinates this special flower creation of our loving Lord Jesus.

How does the male bee know that it needs to find that specific species of orchid to gain the favor of Mrs. Bee? Evolution has no plausible answer. The Creator God of the Bible would say "I made it with all of the equipment and information it needs from its beginning."

Most of you reading this book have probably never heard of these incredible creations of our Creator, the Lord Jesus. There is a reason for this. If something cannot be explained using evolutionary terms, knowledge of it is suppressed. The knowledge is there and it can be found, but it will not make it into the average textbook, your daily newspaper, or the evening news program because most of these forms of communication are part of Satan's Deceptive World System.

Remember what our dear Lord said in His Holy Scripture:

> **For the wrath of God is revealed from heaven against all ungodliness and unrighteousness of men, who hold the truth in unrighteousness;**
>
> **Because that which may be known of God is manifest in them; for God hath shewed *it* unto them. For the invisible things of him from the creation of the world are clearly seen, being understood by the things that are made, *even* his eternal power and Godhead; so that they are without excuse: Because**

that, when they knew God, they glorified *him* not as God, neither were thankful; but became vain in their imaginations, and their foolish heart was darkened. Professing themselves to be wise, they became fools (Romans 1:18-22).

In Satan's World System godless evolution has taken the place of the God of the Bible. Therefore anything that might raise a question as to whether a living animal or plant could actually be here as a result of godless, mindless, non-directed, non-purposeful, accidental, chance processes over millions of years (evolution) is censored out of most public information. This is *DECEPTION*! If the evolutionists, who still control the textbook industry, cannot figure out how to explain an incredible creation of God using evolutionary terms they do not put it in the textbooks. The information about God's creation is out there and can be found with diligent searching, such as, Bombardier beetles, giraffes, Brazil nuts, etc., but most of these things will not be mentioned in the popular textbooks, and if they are discussed it is with only partial information. We need young Christian scholars who will do the research and then write books telling the truth about the great things our Lord has done! One will not become a useful vessel of the Master (II Timothy 2:21) by squandering the God-given days of youth in accommodating the world and all its distractions.

Know ye not that the unrighteous shall not inherit the kingdom of God? Be not deceived: neither fornicators, nor idolaters, nor adulterers, nor effeminate, nor abusers of themselves with mankind, Nor thieves, nor covetous, nor drunkards, nor revilers, nor extortioners, shall inherit the kingdom of God. And such were some of you: but ye are washed, but ye are sanctified, but ye are justified in the name of the Lord Jesus, and by the Spirit of our God (1 Corinthians 6:9-11).

Be not deceived; God is not mocked: for whatsoever a man soweth, that shall he also reap. For he that soweth to his flesh shall of the flesh reap corruption; but he that soweth to the

Spirit shall of the Spirit reap life everlasting.And let us not be weary in well doing: for in due season we shall reap, if we faint not. As we have therefore opportunity, let us do good unto all *men*, especially unto them who are of the household of faith (Galatians 6:7-10).

People study what God has made and because they are ungodly and unrighteous and cannot devise a way to explain something (such as all that is involved with the amazing Brazil nut tree) in evolutionary terms, they just do not tell about it at all. They have been deceived by Satan, the father of lies, as I was for almost half of my life. Evolution seemed so right.

There is a way which seemeth right unto a man, but the end thereof *are* the ways of death. Even in laughter the heart is sorrowful; and the end of that mirth *is* heaviness. The backslider in heart shall be filled with his own ways: and a good man *shall be satisfied* from himself. The simple believeth every word: but the prudent *man* looketh well to his going. A wise *man* feareth, and departeth from evil: but the fool rageth, and is confident (Proverbs 14:12-16).

I was once a "confident" evolutionist! It was a way that seemed so right. How could a convinced evolutionist become a Young Earth Creationist? The first step was to receive the crucified (John 19) and resurrected (1 Corinthians 15) Son of God, the Lord Jesus Christ of the Bible as my personal Savior. With full knowledge of what I was doing and in the presence of pastor Charles Warford, as a twenty-seven year old dentist in the United States Air Force, I prayerfully admitted my lost and sinful state (Romans 3:23) to my Savior Jesus, receiving Him as my Redeemer. Lord Jesus forgave my sin. The Bible says in Isaiah 1:18:

Come now, and let us reason together, saith the LORD: though your sins be as scarlet, they shall be as white as snow; though they be red like crimson, they shall be as wool.

Colossians 2:13, 14 say it like this:

And you, being dead in your sins and the uncircumcision of your flesh, hath he quickened together with him, having forgiven you all trespasses; Blotting out the handwriting of ordinances that was against us, which was contrary to us, and took it out of the way, nailing it to his cross.

The verb "having forgiven" is what is called a Punctiliar Aorist. It means that at a point in time in the past (at the point in the past of receiving Jesus) all of my sins were forgiven and the effects of that go on forever. The "all" of "all trespasses" includes everything and excludes nothing. So when I confessed my sinful state and received the Lord Jesus all my sins were forgiven—past, present and future!

My teenage years were spent in a conservative church. I knew all the right "Christian" words, but my intellectual knowledge about the Bible and Jesus had never been combined with saving faith. I was a lost sinner and a Christian in name only. Being a Christian in name only seems to be the condition of many if not most of the young people in the churches of America. Perhaps that is why the pollsters report that up to 88% of the young folks raised in the church throw out their "Christianity" by the end of four years of college. And it does not seem to matter very much if it is a secular or a Christian college or university. All but a few "Christian" colleges teach some form of evolution. Theistic Evolutionism and Progressive Creationism are popular. As has been stated before, both of these ideas believe in a universe billions of years old and a local river overflow confined to the Mesopotamian Valley in Noah's day. Therefore these schools and colleges are teaching an idea that fights against the true narrative history of origins in the Bible. This confuses our children and builds in them a distrust of God's Word. "If we cannot trust the first chapters of the Bible to be accurate history, why should we trust the rest of it when it talks about such things as 'Virgin Birth' and 'Resurrection'?" Thus, we are losing our kids to other worldviews by the thousands!

Many young people in churches and Christian schools today are on the broad road that leads to destruction and eternal damnation. This is due in a large part to wishy-washy teaching about the Creation and, ultimately, the Creator.

> **Enter ye in at the strait gate: for wide *is* the gate, and broad *is* the way, that leadeth to destruction, and many there be which go in thereat: Because strait *is* the gate, and narrow *is* the way, which leadeth unto life, and few there be that find it** (Matthew 7:13, 14).

Young folks call themselves Christians and know how to talk the acceptable Christian "jargon" but their attitudes and actions are not those of the indwelling Holy Spirit of the Lord Jesus Christ. As my friend Mark Cahill says, "They talk the talk but do not walk the walk!" (*One Thing You Can't Do In Heaven* by Mark Cahill is a book all Christians need to read.)! Our attitudes and actions (behaviors/walk) are the outward display of what we really believe deep down in our hearts. So many are earning the wages of sin which is death.

> **For the wages of sin *is* death; but the gift of God *is* eternal life through Jesus Christ our Lord** (Romans 6:23).

There is an eternal gift waiting for each of us. A gift cannot be earned or worked for or it is not a gift.

> **For by grace are ye saved through faith; and that not of yourselves: *it is* the gift of God: Not of works, lest any man should boast. For we are his workmanship, created in Christ Jesus unto good works, which God hath before ordained that we should walk in them** (Ephesians 2:8-10).

The book of Titus continues this thought:

> **For we ourselves also were sometimes foolish, disobedient, deceived, serving divers lusts and pleasures, living in malice**

and envy, hateful, *and* hating one another. But after that the kindness and love of God our Saviour toward man appeared, Not by works of righteousness which we have done, but according to his mercy he saved us, by the washing of regeneration, and renewing of the Holy Ghost; Which he shed on us abundantly through Jesus Christ our Saviour; That being <u>justified by his grace</u>, we should be made heirs according to the hope of eternal life. *This is* a faithful saying, and these things I will that thou affirm constantly, that they which have believed in God might be careful to <u>maintain good works</u>. These things are good and profitable unto men (Titus 3:3-8).

The God of the Bible Who is the Creator of all has made available to us a free gift. There is nothing that we can do to earn this gift. No amount of church attendance, community service, obedience to laws, philanthropic giving, exemplary parenting, patient tolerance with brothers and sisters or virtuous works will help to pay for this gift. The gift is forgiveness of sins and eternal life. This gift was purchased by the shedding of blood, and death by crucifixion of the eternal Son of the God of the Bible. Jesus Christ died that horrible death to pay for our horrible sins. The fact that our Heavenly Father accepted the death of Jesus as the satisfactory sacrifice for our horrible sins is evidenced by the resurrection of Lord Jesus from the dead. He lives! He took our place on that cross, yours and mine. And so He has every right to say to us that he has a free gift that He wants us to receive—eternal life with Him! We cannot call a gift our own unless we reach out and receive it. Have you prayed and asked the Lord Jesus Christ, our Creator and Redeemer, to forgive your sins? Have you received Him as your personal Savior? It is not necessary to be in church or out on a mountain somewhere to receive Jesus. You can pray and receive Him right now wherever you are.

And all things, whatsoever ye shall ask in prayer, believing, ye shall receive (Matthew 21:22).

What fruit had ye then in those things whereof ye are now ashamed? for the end of those things *is* death. But now being made free from sin, and become servants to God, ye have your fruit unto holiness, and the end everlasting life. For the wages of sin *is* death; but the gift of God *is* eternal life through Jesus Christ our Lord (Romans 6:21-23).

That if thou shalt confess with thy mouth the Lord Jesus, and shalt believe in thine heart that God hath raised him from the dead, thou shalt be saved. For with the heart man believeth unto righteousness; and with the mouth confession is made unto salvation. For the scripture saith, Whosoever believeth on him shall not be ashamed. For there is no difference between the Jew and the Greek: for the same Lord over all is rich unto all that call upon him. For whosoever shall call upon the name of the Lord shall be saved (Romans 10:9-13).

Addendum 2013

Since 2008, even more true science is supporting the creation account as recorded in the Bible. Here are a few brief quotes regarding the elusive evidence for the evolution of man and more evidence supporting a global flood. The evolutionists are now saying: "We thought we had just about nailed human evolution, now everything is up for grabs again" (Ed Yong, "Our Hybrid Origins," New Scientist, July 30, 2011, 35).   "The origin of our own genus [human] remains frustratingly unclear" (Bernard Wood, 2011, "Did early Homo migrate 'out of' or 'in to' Africa?," Proceedings of the National Academy of Sciences,108 (26): 10375). Evidence for the evolution of man from primates over millions of years is losing credibility even among evolutionists.

Progressive Creationists and Theistic Evolutionists teach a "local river overflow" and not a global flood in Noah's day, but now evolutionists are saying, "It [Earth] would have almost been an ocean world" (Louis Bergeron, "Stanford study: Earth's early ocean cooled more than a billion years earlier than thought," Stanford University press release, November 11, 2009). "However, some recent studies suggest that water may have covered Earth's entire surface for some 200 million years before the continents emerged" (Tom Garrison, 2013, Oceanography, Belmont, CA: Brooks/Cole, 16). So the evolutionists are now saying that Earth was once covered with water—their timing is way off, but their global flood evidence supports Biblical history. A flood covered the entire earth in Noah's day (Genesis 6-8) and God created man from dust (Genesis 2:7). We can believe the Bible!